MODI STOLE MY MASK

THE TRUTH ABOUT INDIA'S COVID CRISIS

AMIT BAGARIA
&
SAVIO RODRIGUES

गरुड

Published by
Garuda Prakashan Private Limited
Gurugram, India

www.garudabooks.com

First published in India 2021

ISBN: 978-1-942426-55-4

Cover Design: Aditi Shah

Printed in India

Contents

Other Books by Amit Bagaria

1914 NaMo or MoNa
Why is 2019 not 2014?

DEMYTHSIFYING MYTHS
Demystifying 18 Myths about India

OK TATA
Why is Tata in the ICU?

72@72
72 Unfinished Things India@72 Needs to Do

Mr. President...Yes, Prime Minister

USAma
Is USA the World's Largest Terrorist?

I-SPY
A Peep into the World of Spies

SPIES, LIES & RED TAPE
A Spy-Military-Political Fiction Thriller

The Tiger Gets New Teeth
What does the PM do when the IB, RAW, and
the NIA are constantly failing to do their jobs?

POK भारत में वापस
देशभक्ति और रोमांच से भरपूर उपन्यास

CONGRESS-*MUKT* BHARAT
Is the Modi Era the End of Congress

Previews

"While the title is perhaps a sardonic barb at the AMB (the authors' acronym for the anti-Modi brigade), the book is by no means an apologists' tome. It is an extremely critical appraisal of the second wave of COVID-19 and does not spare the PM or the government for their lapses. On the other hand, it is trenchant when it deals with myths, fake news and concocted statistics surrounding the March-May 2021 surge, a reflection of the authors' ire at the cynical politicization of the pandemic. The issues dealt with are wide-ranging and at the core of the raging debate over the second wave causes: vaccine hesitancy and later shortages; the paucity of hospital beds, ventilators, and oxygen supply; the efficacy of the responses of different states; India's plight qua other countries and the adequacy of the govt's efforts on these and other fronts. The authors state their case on every issue with robust empiricism. The book is a statistician's delight, The only hints of the author's predilections are in the sections titled 'Was the second wave planned?' and 'Pharma Industry and Hospitals anti Modi?' but even here the case is cogently argued, and the answers left to the reader. In sum this sharp book serves the public interest in objectively debunking contemporary misconceptions regarding the reasons for the second wave. It is a compelling read. If you don't read it, you do so at the peril of being singularly misinformed."

Mahesh Jethmalani
Rajya Sabha MP; Senior Advocate, Bombay High Court

"An unbiased, honest, comprehensive and fearless account of the politics surrounding the second wave of COVID-19 in India."

Ashwin Sanghi
New York Times Bestselling Author of *Private India* (Sold in the USA as *City on Fire*) and Private Delhi (Sold in the USA as *Count to Ten*); *Forbes India* Celebrity 100 List

"A meticulously researched and extensively documented account of the Modi administration's response to the Covid-19 pandemic. Compulsory reading for those who wish to understand how India faced up to a crisis of unprecedented proportions."

Dr Makarand R Paranjape
Professor; Researcher; Author; Editor; Columnist; Essayist; Poet
Director, Indian Institute of Advance Study, Shimla

"A truly extraordinary book that studies the entire impact of the Covid-19 pandemic on India and how PM Modi and his government handled this crisis! The pandemic quickly became a political issue to beat up the government and malign India, with the Global Left, their fellow travelers in India, Vulture Journalists and assorted politicians joining in creating fake and one-sided narratives to derive a political advantage! The second wave was sudden, unexpected, and very severe, creating an unprecedented crisis, much beyond the capacity of any government! The authors use data and analytics to go behind the cacophony and expose the forces who created fear and sought to blame one person! A must read for all Indian citizens."

TV Mohandas Pai
Chairman, Aarin Capital Partners

"Amit Bagaria and Savio Rodrigues in 'Modi Stole My Mask' weave a detailed, insightful and academically-inclined narrative about India and the manner in which it has handled the Covid crisis. What is remarkable about this book is the in-depth analysis which the authors have done in over 960 man-hours of painstaking research. Very rarely do people capture life-altering events with such alacrity as Amit and Savio have done. In many ways, this is not just a book about Modi, or about Covid but indeed about us Indians and the pulls and pressures of being the world's largest and often chaotic democracy."

Suhel Seth
Actor; Author; Columnist; TV Panellist; Strategic Brand Marketing Consultant

"The 'Dummy's Guide to the Covid Controversy'. A racy, data packed confirmation & rebuttal on every possible facet of Covid-induced politics. Read the book to clear your mind which has been confused by #COVIDIOTS."

Dr Ratan Sharda
Author, Biographer, Columnist; TV Panellist; ERP Consultant

"WARNING: Do Not Read This Book If You Don't Want to Know the Truth Behind India's devastating Covid-19 second wave! Authors Amit Bagaria and Savio Rodrigues deftly navigate through reams of research material and hard data to unmask the sinister conspiracy behind India's sudden surge of Covid-19 in the dreaded second wave. 'Modi Stole My Mask' neatly puts together multiple pieces of the gigantic jigsaw puzzle of the second wave, starting from the anti-CAA protests and farmer agitation to exposing the artificially created oxygen shortages and the open anti-India bias exhibited by the media. As the author duo state, the pandemic is as much 'war on India as much as it is a war on the world'. The book is a riveting read that reveals exactly how the events unfolded, and how the entire anti-Modi brigade used the second wave of pandemic to defame India and to demonise one man, Narendra Modi!"

Shefali Vaidya
Author; Speaker; Fellow, Ananta Leadership Program; Convenor, Indic Academy

"A very well researched and strongly opinionated book. Due to the Covid crisis, there is not a single family in India who hasn't lost a family member or a friend, so it's natural for us to feel depressed. The unbearable grief is the common thread that binds us all. But along with that it's very easy to get carried away in a one-sided narrative of everything-is-doomed-forever-in-India. And once you are in that kind of mood swing, it is natural for the other side of the spectrum to exploit that emotional vulnerability. The authors have clearly mentioned right in the start that they are in no way saying that the Govt. is not to be blamed for the crisis and they are not suggesting that things did not go out of hand. They certainly did. But that is not stopping them from looking at the big picture and arguing that all is not lost, and we shall overcome. Even if you disagree with their strong opinions, you should read the book and appreciate it just for the analysis of all the Covid related databases compiled in one single place."

Yashwant Deshmukh
Founder–Deshmukh, CVoter International

"MODI STOLE MY MASK is a brutal compendium of the accumulated misreporting that has plagued the media in India through the COVID-19 crisis. It focuses on how command responsibility & fault lines & policy decisions were constantly misreported without correction or context, by reporters and editors who failed at every step to do even basic due diligence. Needless to say, comparative analyses or studies on local applicability were non-existent and the ever-present problem of the blurring of the lines between opinion & news were blatantly discarded. The thesis in this book is essential to understanding the exacerbator role the media played through the crisis."

Abhijit Iyer-Mitra
Senior Fellow, Institute of Peace and Conflict Studies, New Delhi
Ex-Visiting Fellow, Sandia National Laboratories (USA) & The Stimson Centre (USA)

"MODI STOLE MY MASK is an essential read for anyone who cares to know about why people behaved the way they did during the Pandemic. The authors have dwelt deep into each & every issue using statistics & numbers. It gives you clues about whether the Second Wave was planned & strategized. The book has eloquently exposed journalists & politicians who have tried the bake their bread on the sacred pyres of our beloved ones. Indian COVID-19 data is compared with other major countries like the USA. While American journals & dailies would make you believe that India is on its knees, this book gives you hope by showing how well we are countering the battle. Do not miss the important chapter about the possibility of the Coronavirus (which causes COVID-19) being the result of a Bioweapon."

Aabhas Maldahiyar, B.Arch.
Author; Columnist; Architect & Urban Designer

"An exquisite book reflecting on the rudderless leadership of money driven dynasts and the extent they would go to grab power by propaganda to demolish/ character assassinate the leadership of our elected government, sponsored by the likes of China to fuel their hideous plans to conquer world economy. The book sheds light on the operational toolkit used by the dynasts and their ecosystem to create what Mr. Dynast himself tweeted about – 'fear'. The fear mongering stands exposed. The book explains why people abstained from vaccination, the greedy nexus of the dynasts, and the foreign dark hands. The questions of who instigated such a large scale of migration and who conveniently used the international media to film at cremation grounds to create divide in the society is answered. A must read for all Indians to understand the networking of the dark forces profiteering for the last 60 years, whose scams stand at mammoth sizes. India has no space for such corrupt people. Let the truth reach the common man. I congratulate the authors for the brilliant masterpiece and the work put in."

Tom Vadakkan
National Spokesperson, BJP; Former AICC Secretary, Media Department Member and National Spokesperson of the Congress party

"The authors have outdone themselves with artistry of weaving hard hitting and superbly researched facts with underlying social political issues of India during the 'COVIDIAN' era. 'Modi stole my Mask' is a stellar new age offering to today's volatile geopolitics and India's perplexing social dynamics. It will remain a Go-To Bible for anyone who would want an encyclopedic inspection about why and how India behaved the way it did during the pandemic. An extremely informed commentary on both the success and errors of the Modi government, it's a must read for anyone who would enjoy arsenal for a balanced debate as well as remain cognizant of India's true fight against COVID-19."

Shweta Satpathy
Brand Evangelist & International Marketing Expert

"Such is the excellent analysis of data that NO ONE can punch holes in. They detail Congress's criminal bogey on vaccine-funding, efficacy, not installing PM CARES Fund-given made-in-India ventilators; as well as AAP misappropriating injections and raising bogey of scarce oxygen. Authors punch hole on NaMo's electioneering and brings facts on Central Vista Project. Honest that Kumbh was avoidable but question why same not spoken about Farmer's protests & Eid congregations. The authors conclude that COVID-19 is genetically engineered by China to sabotage the current world order with Congress a complicity."

Yogesh Jain
Business Strategy and Management Systems Consultant

"Exemplary research and thorough understanding of international and Indian politics makes this book a stellar read. Amit & Savio address the sinister plot that the Congress party hatched throughout its time as a decimated opposition in contrast to PM Modi's key achievements during the pandemic. The book does justice to highlight the Left media that propagates a shallow narrative against the national interest and salutes the unconditional support of the Indian Armed Forces in battling the virus."

Subhajit Paul
MA in Media: Former Journalist with *Reuters*; *Republic TV* Reporter

"What really happened between April and June? Was it a manufactured crisis? Did Modi finally fail to lead or were Anti-India forces finally able to create a crisis to make Modi look like a failed leader? If you are seeking real facts, this is THE book for you. It's so gripping that I read it without pause and I could see the days from April onwards unfold with facts emerging. The book is extremely detailed with graphs and references. It does a great job at peeling the layers and exposing the enemies within. It also touches on issues of medical negligence and malpractice which we always end up shoving under the carpet. In the age of media manipulation and post truth, this book does an excellent job of exposing how Anti-India forces got together to push the nation towards a massive crisis."

Poli Gupta
Software Professional

"Amazing book with the real truth told with facts and figures — thus silencing sold out journalists and politicians. It reminded me of Arthur Hailey's books, very gripping this one too! A MUST READ FOR ALL."

Raja Bodapati
Grandson of a Freedom Fighter; LIC employee; Formerly with Tata Group

"Logically organized research-based content with facts. There will always be fearless & honest minds like Amit & Savio in every field for all the good that happens in the world despite the adharma that prevails through toxic ecosystems."

Sangita Iyer
Author; Documentary Filmmaker; Positive Psychology & Leadership Training Expert

"Stupendous work. A data driven view on the horrors that were meticulously unleashed upon us mercilessly & unabashedly. Beta may lie ... but data cannot."

Ullas Ramakrishnan
Associate Professor (Business Strategy & International Business),
Dhruva College of Management, Hyderabad

"It's rare in India to find well researched books. It's even rarer to find well researched books on contentious political issues. And it is rarest to find well researched books on contemporary/current affairs. I just could not believe that Amit and Savio have written this book when the controversy is alive and is a hot trending topic. But it's not a book written in a hurry. With more than 1,000 hours of painstaking research, and it's not a third person perspective. Both Amit & Savio have been affected by this 'once in a century pandemic' and have been both at receiving and giving ends. It's a firsthand analysis. That's why they don't make the mistake of justifying the Modi government, nor do they condemn its efforts without any factual support. This book has been extremely useful to me as it cleared many doubts in my mind. This is not just a book but a microscopic view of politics around Covid. Read it. Because it's written by two 'angry' people. In anger, people speak from their hearts. And this book is an example of that. Read it like the author-duo say: "We are angry, and thus we write ... because the pen is mightier than the sword."

Vivek Ranjan Agnihotri
National Award Winning Filmmaker; Bestselling Author

"This is the second book by Amit that I read and of course I regularly read Savio's articles in *Goa Chronicle*. It was great to see that both of them came together to write this much needed and extremely timely book. Being a former journalist myself, I was shocked to see my colleagues (especially Indian ones) write (and report) the kind of negative stories they did, for the sole purpose of maligning Modiji. Their motivation and purpose are not hidden from anyone with even basic IQ. Therefore, I want to thank Amit and Savio to bring out the truth based on data on facts, and data doesn't lie!"

Shazia Ilmi
National Spokesperson, BJP; Social Activist; Filmmaker;
Former National Executive Member, AAP; Former Anchor, Star News

Abbreviations

AAP   Aam Aadmi Party, headed by Delhi CM Arvind Kejriwal

AIIMS   All India Institutes of Medical Sciences, a chain of 22 GOI-owned medical colleges-cum-super specialty referral hospitals.

AMB   Anti Modi Brigade

BB   Bharat Biotech International Ltd. is India's second largest manufacturer of COVID-19 vaccines, and the only one which developed its COVAXIN vaccine without foreign technology.

CM   Chief Minister of an Indian state

DRDO   Defence Research and Development Organisation, India

GOI   Government of India

ICMR   Indian Council of Medical Research

MoHFW   Ministry of Health and Family Welfare, GOI

PM   Prime Minister

POTUS   President of the United States

SII   Serum Institute of India Pvt. Ltd. is India's largest manufacturer of COVID-19 vaccines, and the world's largest manufacturer of all types of vaccines. It makes COVISHIELD under license from UK-based AstraZeneca.

TMC   Trinamool Congress party headed by West Bengal Chief Minister Mamata Banerjee

WHO   The World Health Organization is an agency of the United Nations responsible for international public health.

Note from the Authors

It has taken us over 1,170 hours of painstaking work to research and write this book, very often burning the midnight oil; so we are grateful that you have bought a copy and hope you will enjoy reading it. We hope you will get at least some information you may not have previously had.

Amit has lost two close family members to COVID-19. Both his parents were hospitalized for over a week in April 2021. His son had Covid in October 2020, and over 75 family members and close friends had it at some time or the other, so he too is affected by this once-in-a-century pandemic. However, he is a realistic person who studies facts and data before reaching conclusions.

During the first wave of the pandemic, on most days Savio would get phone calls requesting for financial assistance or a job. In the second-wave, however, he got calls from people asking for hospital beds, oxygen concentrators and financial assistance. Sadly, even after his NGO managed to find aid for people, they could not save some lives.

There is no balm to soothe and calm the pain of someone who has lost a loved one in a biological war that has come at our doorstep. This is war on India as much as it is a war on the world. We must fight it with facts and data. We must expose the truth.

Ever since April 6, 2021, when the number of people infected with COVID-19 (the SARS-CoV-2 virus) crossed one lakh for the first time since the pandemic 'officially' started in India in February 2020, people started blaming Prime Minister Narendra Modi for India's 'second wave' of COVID-19.

When the daily case count crossed 1.5 lakh just four days later (April 10), the voices became a little louder. These were not just on TV screens, but also posts on social media (especially Twitter), and articles in Indian and foreign media (newspapers as well as news websites). Those not active on Twitter need to know that Twitter is a very important social space for political discourse in India, with an estimated 80 million accounts, ~55 million MAUs or monthly active users (as per App Annie), and almost 12 million hours of time spent per day by these MAUs.

Fast forward to just five days later and these voices gained additional energy and momentum, as India crossed the unfortunate milestone of two lakh cases in a single day. **Yes, India had doubled its daily case count in just nine days in the first half of April.**

This must be seen in the context that the daily case count had peaked at below a lakh (97,859) during the 'first wave', on September 16, 2020. Of course, the second wave was much worse.

India crossed three lakh cases on April 21, 2021, the number of people infected that day being 2.74 times the number recorded just 15 days earlier.

By that time, India already had severe shortages of hospital beds (normal beds as well as ICU beds with or without a ventilator), medical oxygen (one of the first things a COVID-19 patient needs after the lungs are affected), and Remdesivir (an antiviral medication first developed in 2009 as a treatment for Hepatitis C, and subsequently investigated for the Ebola virus and the Marburg virus, before being 'studied' as a post-infection treatment for COVID-19).

The anti-Modi brigade (we shall also refer to them as 'the AMB' throughout this book) now got a huge supply of additional arsenal to aim at India's prime minister.

The same prime minister (PM) who had won a larger mandate from India's 61.3 crore voters less than two years earlier, who had been credited across the world a year earlier for handling the pandemic very well, and who had been applauded just a couple of months earlier by more than 50 world leaders for helping them combat the disease in their own countries, as India had exported (or even donated) vaccines to more than 90 countries.

Most of the attacks on India's PM and his government (Central Govt. or GOI or 'the Centre')—and therefore on India as a whole—did not come from China or Pakistan. It came from within—from political opponents of Modi and the Bharatiya Janata Party (BJP) and their voters/ fans, from journalists and media houses that have always been against Modi/BJP, from hundreds of armchair 'experts' who took on Modi and the BJP on TV debates and thousands more through social media, especially Twitter.

Needless to say, such people are 'experts' on everything, including epidemiology, healthcare management, manufacturing, logistics and distribution, statistics, data science, and even how a nation of 139.2 crore people should be administered!

However, there was a new phenomenon this time. Tens of lakhs of people who had till 2020 or even March 2021 been Modi supporters, turned against him. Out of about 750 people in our combined WhatsApp groups, about 500 were Modi supporters until March 2021. Today, on May 15, we can hardly find 75 or so. Scores of people sent WhatsApp messages saying "Modi Must Resign".

India recorded 3,54,658 cases on April 25, 2021, which was ~3.62 times higher than the first wave peak of 97,859 reached on September 16, 2020. The anti-Modi, anti-GOI, and anti-BJP voices grew even louder, compounded by the undeniable fact that the oxygen crisis had gotten much worse between April 21 and 25, 2021.

On April 18, Amit decided to write this book (his 13th book in English and 17th book if you count his Hindi books) as he was deeply pained to see most politicians waste precious time and energy to squabble against each other in this time of grave crisis, which harms India more than China and Pakistan ever can. Fifteen days later, Savio joined him as a co-author.

Indian politicians all came together as 'one' when China attacked us in 1962, and again during the Indo-Pak wars of 1965, 1971, and 1999. In the recent Israel-Hamas conflict, all opposition politicians united with the then Israeli Prime Minister Benjamin Netanyahu.

Don't (most) Indian citizens come together when we play a cricket match against Pakistan? Alas, a lot has changed in the last two decades, and unfortunately it has changed for the worse.

We are angry, and thus we write ... because, the pen is mightier than the sword.

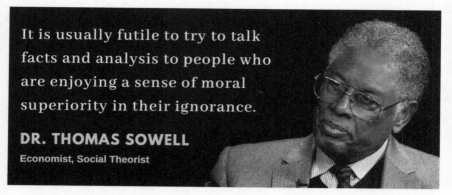

It is usually futile to try to talk facts and analysis to people who are enjoying a sense of moral superiority in their ignorance.

DR. THOMAS SOWELL
Economist, Social Theorist

Even Dr Antony Fauci, chief medical advisor to POTUS said on May 7, 2021, to an Indian TV channel that "*the enemy is the Coronavirus, and people of different political parties or with different ideologies should stop fighting with each other at this time of crisis.*" When Fauci was a member of the White House Coronavirus Task Force under President Trump, India's Leftist media mocked him with all kinds of memes and abuses! However, after new President Joe Biden appointed him as chief medical advisor, Fauci has become everyone's hero! Is it wrong for us to say that such media consists of spineless persons?

We are in no way implying that Modi or the Central Government are not to blame for the utter lack of preparation or the management of the COVID-19 second wave, which had to come some day or the other, because hardly any country has been able to escape it. As Chief Executive, the primary blame must definitely go to Modi.

Modi's IQ and wisdom are arguably better than 85% of all Indians and 95% of all Indian politicians—why did he listen to advise from others, and not anticipate a devastating second wave guided by his own wisdom?

But is Modi the only one to blame? Or is there a shared blame? Who all are the culprits? Is there a 'larger story' behind this second wave?

This book discusses all of that ... and more.

We are not going to discuss the Kumbh Mela in this book, as we firmly believe the *mela* should have been indefinitely postponed, or even cancelled. But we must add that other religious gatherings were also super-spreader events, including the Ramzan gatherings and Eid celebrations across India, and some Christian gatherings, especially in Kerala. Muslim mobs doing *namaz* pelted stones on the police at Hyderabad, Jaipur, Kapadvanj in Gujarat, and many other places. There was a huge crowd at the funeral of Congress's Rajasthan minister Saleh Mohammad's father Maulana Gazi Fakir at Jaisalmer on April 27, when the second wave had already started peaking.

What about the farmer protests around Delhi, in Punjab, Haryana, and Western UP? Are those protestors immune from COVID-19 and also don't spread the disease?

Although many people on Twitter, LinkedIn, and WhatsApp have asked us to also write on the possible long-term solutions to improve India's healthcare infrastructure and systems, so that we don't face such a national crisis again, we shall unfortunately not be covering that topic in this book. It will perhaps become the subject for another book, and if we do decide to write one, we will seek to collaborate with better-qualified experts on the subject.

It is possible that you have read some articles by Amit Bagaria on some of the topics covered in this book, which were published in different online news websites, including *GoaChronicle*, *tfipost*, and *News Bharati*, but please do not skip any of those chapters, as they have many more facts and information than Amit's previously-published articles.

Meanwhile, 16 lions at different zoos or safari parks at Chennai, Hyderabad, and Etawah (UP) were tested COVID-positive. Maybe Modi will have 16 real lions contesting against him in 2024.

The Second Wave

On the 67th day of the second wave of COVID-19 in India, the number of cases were already **4.23 times (4,14,182 compared with 97,859) the peak cases during the first wave (April–December 2020)**. Look at it in context of 20 other most affected countries (with minimum 1.5 million or 15 lakh cases) in this chart.

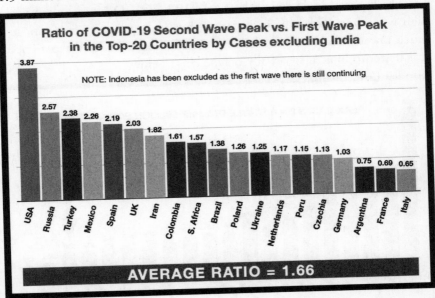

The comparison of the total number of cases/deaths/tests/vaccinated people, and other related statistics, has to be in terms of the number of cases per million (one million = 10 lakhs) population, as **there is no other way to compare data**. We cannot expect numbers in a huge country like India to be the same as Italy with 4.34% of India's population, Brazil with 15.37%, or even the US with 23.9% of India's population.

The daily circulation of *The Times of India* is more than double of the UK's largest newspaper *Metro*; almost 1.78 times higher than the US's largest newspaper *USA Today*; 5.95 times, 20.4 times, and 32.5 times higher than the favourites of India's Leftists/liberals *The New York Times* (USA), *The Guardian* (UK), and *The Australian*, respectively; not because more Indians read English newspapers, but because India has so many more people. The Indian Railways has 10.1 times more passenger-kilometres of traffic than the Russian Railways as India's population is 9.53 times higher than Russia's.

Therefore, **it is but natural that India will see many more people get sick from a pandemic than much smaller countries.**

If China disclosed COVID-19 data honestly, we would have some 'real' comparisons, but China hasn't done so—not that anyone with even an average IQ expects them to.

The highest single day peak of 4,14,182 COVID-19 cases looks very high when you look at it in isolation, but in terms of population, it is much lower than the peaks that many other countries have experienced. It is better to look at it visually on the chart below.

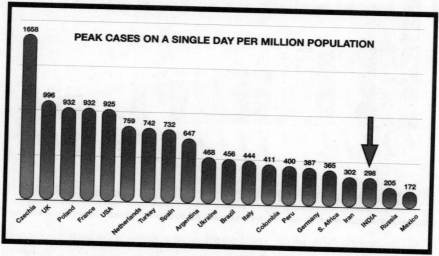

For India to match the average (739.3) of the seven most developed countries in the above chart (USA, UK, Germany, France, Netherlands, Italy, and Spain), we would need to record 10.29 lakh (1.029 million)

cases on a single day. If that happens, we can say goodbye to all our loved ones and thank God for whatever he gave us in our lives.

Now let us move on to the main issue. **Should India have guessed that the second wave will have 4.23 times higher peak daily cases than the first wave** (even higher than what happened in the US, which tops the chart on the first page of this chapter)? Or should India have prepared for the second wave to have on an average 1.66 times the number of peak cases as the first wave, like it happened in 19 of the other Top-20 countries? In fact, if one excludes the US as being an outlier, the average for the other 18 countries comes further down to 1.27.

If you agree that 1.66 seems to be the more pragmatic answer, then India's new COVID-19 cases on May 5, 2021, would have been 1,62,446 instead of 4,14,182. If this were indeed the case, **we would not have the multipronged crisis of the shortage of vaccines, hospital beds, oxygen, Remdesivir, Tocilizumab, or other drugs, of the same magnitude that we actually did.** But then, *"If wishes were horses, beggars would ride,"* says the 493-year-old Scottish proverb.

Some of these countries—Turkey, Colombia, Spain, Argentina, Peru, Netherlands, and Czechia—are already experiencing a third wave.

India conducted an average of ~11.7 lakh (1.17 million) tests per day during the first wave peak and an average of ~17 lakh tests during the second wave peak. Therefore, the testing has gone up ~1.45 times. As cases have gone up by a much larger 4.23 times, it is obvious that the TPR or Test Positivity Ratio (number tested positive out of total number tested) this time is much higher. Did any expert predict that this would happen?

After all, the Modi government does not have an algorithm that predicts the potential increase in numbers or the higher severity and transmission rates, as none is available.

Look at the chart below. It is scary. The only people who can be happy with a chart that looks like this after February 2021 are stock market investors if it shows the market index, or businessmen/ corporate managers if it shows their sales or profits. The first wave looks like a hillock which even an unhealthy person can climb, whereas the second wave looks like Mount Everest.

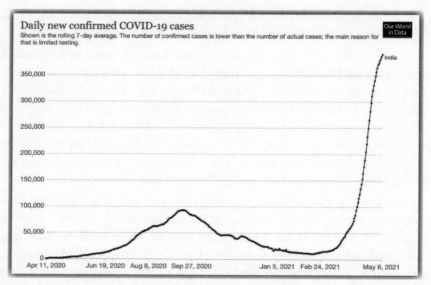

But, as the 195-year-old British phrase says, **"What goes up, must come down,"** and that is what this same chart looked like just 15 days later. Needless to say, people believe that Modi caused the steep rise in numbers; but was not responsible in any way for the steep fall. Facts in this book will prove otherwise. However, many state CMs who imposed strict lockdowns should also be credited for the fall, which has been equally steep as the rise.

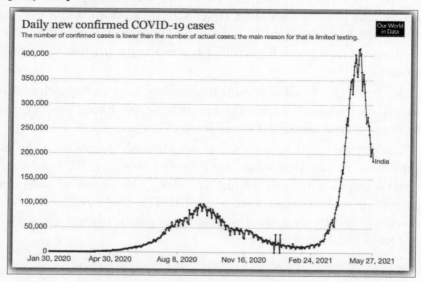

Another thing differentiates the second wave from the first wave. Most of the cases during the second wave are of a different strain (or a double/triple mutant), which are killing people faster, and also affecting (including killing) younger people, than the first wave. In the second wave, double- and triple-mutant variants of the virus—referring to two or three strains of the coronavirus combining to form a new variant— widely spread across the country. It's not that this is completely shocking, as countries that experienced the second wave before India had already shared their own similar experiences publicly.

As **Adar Poonawalla**, CEO of SII told the UK-based newspaper, *The Times*, *"**I don't think even God could have forecast it was going to get this bad** … I thought, we've done our bit [before the second surge began]. We'd struggled through 2020 to get everything ready. I thought I could put my feet up and take a vacation, but it's been the exact opposite. It's been chaotic."*

Something else was weird about India's second wave. **The cases went up 32.76 times in 60 days from March 1 to April 30, 2021.** This chart has the comparison with the 20 most affected countries in number of cumulative cases. In the case of Argentina and Peru, the data is for the third wave, as there was very little time gap between the first two waves in both countries. Similarly, data for Czechia and Netherlands is for the first wave, as the gap between the first and second waves was too short.

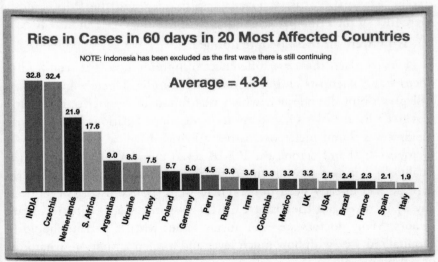

Rise in Cases in 60 days in 20 Most Affected Countries

NOTE: Indonesia has been excluded as the first wave there is still continuing

Average = 4.34

32.8 32.4 21.9 17.6 9.0 8.5 7.5 5.7 5.0 4.5 3.9 3.5 3.3 3.2 3.2 2.5 2.4 2.3 2.1 1.9

INDIA Czechia Netherlands S. Africa Argentina Ukraine Turkey Poland Germany Peru Russia Iran Colombia Mexico UK USA Brazil France Spain Italy

We see several dozen leading doctors giving *'gyan'* on TV every day, including Chairmen or CEOs of leading standalone hospitals or hospital chains. Many have also been giving interviews to the print media, both Indian and foreign. Even cardiac (heart) surgeons are doling out *gyan* on a disease which has nothing to do with their medical specialty. Many 'reputed' doctors have been advising the GOI on measures to be taken to combat COVID-19 for the last year or so. Others who were not called upon for their advice could have very easily volunteered their 'expertise' to the GOI.

Can any of them prove (with evidence that will stand in a court of law) that they warned the government that the second wave (within 67 days) will have 4.23 times the peak number of cases as the first wave, or that cases will shoot up 32.76 times in just two months? If someone can, **we, the authors, will stand up and salute him/her, and suggest to the PM that s/he should be made India's health minister!**

Why didn't the Indian Medical Association (IMA), the country's leading body of doctors with over 330,000 members, petition the Election Commission (or even the Supreme Court) to postpone the state assembly elections held in four states and one UT during March-April 2021?

Apart from experts in leading government hospitals such as AIIMS in New Delhi, amongst others, leading private hospitals/chains such as Apollo, Manipal, Fortis, Narayana Health, etc., and the IMA, there is the Office of the Principal Scientific Advisor to the GOI, and the ICMR.

WTF were all these people doing?

Even to date, there are differences of opinion even between leading doctors and scientists and/or researchers in India. Doctors in India are still prescribing Remdesivir, which was found to be ineffective against Covid-19 by the WHO, and by most developed nations. Even plasma therapy was found ineffective as per a British Medical Journal study of October 2020 and it took the ICMR seven months (May 18, 2021) to finally drop it as a recommended treatment protocol in India. But the damage had already been done. There were thousands of tweets every day by relatives and friends of COVID-19 patients appealing to plasma donors. Many doctors are even unsure about when a patient should be hospitalised, i.e., with how much fever and oxygen saturation, what kind of symptoms, etc.

But no one has the guts to speak up against doctors in India. After all, we don't address aircraft pilots or a railway engine driver as 'Pilot sahib' or 'Engineer sahib' even though our life is in their hands while we are traveling in the vehicles being steered by them. But we address doctors as 'Doctor sahib'. Why shouldn't we question them? Are we afraid that they won't treat us when we are sick?

Then there is the national scientific task force on COVID-19, which includes the cabinet secretary, the health secretary, the home secretary, the principal secretary to the PM, two advisors to the PM, and leading scientists. The NITI Aayog's member for health, the secretary, health research, and the director-general of the ICMR are supposed to regularly interact with the task force.

This task force did not even meet once during February and March 2021. This year the taskforce met on January 11, and then on April 15 and 21, 2021, after India was hit by the surge in cases. The number of daily reported cases had already gone up to 1,85,086 on April 13, compared with 12,482 on January 11, 2021, a 14.8x increase. By the time the task force met for the first time in April, the cases had shot up to 1,99,569, or more than double the first wave peak.

Even as the second wave was at or near its peak, the principal scientific advisor (PSA) to the GOI Dr K Vijay Raghavan said that a third wave is inevitable, but the timing could not be predicted. He also said that *"usually the second wave is expected to be smaller than the first."* This was not true for 17 of the 20 most affected countries. Two days later, the PSA said that a third wave could be prevented. He should be immediately sacked.

Virologist Dr V Ravi warned that the third wave of COVID-19 will hit children in a big way and it is time for both the Centre and state governments to chalk out strategies and gear up to handle the situation between October and December 2021. What should we do to protect 35.92 crore 1–14 year olds from the third wave, Dr Ravi? Send them to New Zealand, where Jacinda Ardern can quarantine them? As their population is only 48.6 lakhs, if they run out of space, she can send them to neighbouring Australia which has plenty of open desert land.

People want Jacinda to become the PM of India, when her experience is limited to running a country with 28.7% and 65.3% of Bengaluru's and Surat's population, respectively. **There is no shortage of idiots (or Covidiots) in our country.**

CONCLUSIONS

- India has just experienced one of the most severe second waves of Covid-19 in the world.

- Officials of the Health Ministry, Science & Technology Ministry, Office of the Principal Scientific Advisor, ICMR, and thousands of medical 'experts' failed to predict the dates or gravity of India's second wave of Covid-19.

- The PM — being a wise man — should not have listened to them, and should have taken all decisions required to prepare well in advance.

Health Comes First

INDIAN LIVES MATTER

Co-vultures

As tens of thousands people were dying and **India's healthcare infrastructure itself was in the ICU**, a few hundred "covultures" were busy making money from the pandemic. Pulse oximeters, oxygen cylinders, oxygen concentrators, drugs such as Remdesivir, Tocilizumab, and Bevacizumab, even ambulance rides were being black marketed.

In Delhi, ambulance owners were charging ₹15,000–40,000 for a 3–5 km journey. Similar cases were reported in several other cities and towns, but the amounts did not reach ₹40,000 anywhere else. Delhi, being the city where maximum 'cut money' has changed hands until 2014, obviously has the maximum black money and thus the highest affordability. Here are some examples of other crucial items being black marketed during this crisis.

ITEM	Normal Price	Black-market Price
3-km Ambulance Journey	₹900–1,000	₹5,000–10,000
Pulse Oximeter	₹900–2,000	₹4,000–8,000
Oxygen Flow Meter	₹800–1,200	₹6,000–12,000
Remdesivir (100mg Vial)	₹900–3,490	₹14,000–45,000
Oxygen Cylinder	₹5,000–19,750	₹30,000–95,000
Oxygen Concentrator	₹16,000–68,000	₹50,000–160,000
Tocilizumab 400mg	₹32,480–40,600	₹100,000–200,000
Hospital Bed (normal)	₹6,000–17,500	₹15,000–50,000
Hospital Bed (ICU)	₹12,500–40,000	₹30,000–125,000

More than 2.74 crore spurious Remdesivir vials were seized by police at several places up to May 1, 2021, as they contained just saline water or tap water. The same was the case with Tocilizumab, although in smaller quantities. Some hospitals in Delhi, Hyderabad, Chennai, Pune, and other cities were selling or even auctioning Remdesivir and Tocilizumab, at 2x to 6x the actual prices. They were also black-marketing other items.

When Amit was a hospital consultant, he had come across the shocking fact that organs such as eyes (cornea) and kidneys which had been donated, were 'sold' to rich people in the waiting list, even at leading hospitals such as AIIMS Delhi. Some doctors who were involved went on to become leading healthcare 'businessmen' and were even funded by globally-reputed Private Equity funds. His disgust was one of the reasons he left the sector. The Amazon Prime Video TV show "Breathe" starring South Indian star Madhavan is a good example of to what extent human beings can go to get organs for their loved ones.

"If independence is granted to India, power will go to the hands of rascals, rogues, freebooters; all Indian leaders will be of low calibre and men of straw. They will have sweet tongues and silly hearts. They will fight amongst themselves for power and India will be lost in political squabbles," leader of the opposition Sir Winston Churchill said when Prime Minister Sir Clement Attlee announced in February 1947 in the British House of Commons (lower house of the UK parliament) that India was being granted independence. Churchill was a former PM (May 1940 to July 1945) then and became PM again (October 1951 to April 1955) for a second term.

In 1921, C. Rajagopalachari said, *"We all ought to know that swaraj (self-rule) will not at once or, I think, even for a long time to come, be better government or greater happiness for the people. Elections and their corruptions, injustice, and the power and tyranny of wealth, and inefficiency of administration, will make a hell of life as soon as freedom is given to us."* Rajaji was the first and last 'Indian' Governor General of India, apart from having held several other significant posts such as first CM of Madras State, first Governor of West Bengal, and second Home Minister of India.

On April 27, 2021, Ghaziabad Police arrested the CEO of Hyatt Health Insurance, Dr Mohammad Altamash, and his two accomplices, Kumail Akram and Jazib Ali, with 70 vials of Remdesivir and over ₹30 crores in cash. During his interrogation, Altamash said that he was selling Remdesivir injections for ₹20,000-40,000 and Actamera injections for ₹1-2 lakhs. Congress's Prashant Parashar was part of a fake Remdesivir racket in Indore. Shiv Sena's Chandrakant Raghuvanshi and BJP MP Sujay Vikhe Patil stocked up hundreds of Remdesivir vials.

On May 5, the Bengaluru Police arrested social worker Nethravathy (40), and her nephew Rohith Kumar (22), for their role in the (alleged) fraud in the allotment of over 4,000 beds in return for money from COVID-19 patients in the city. They were 'selling' beds meant for others who had tested positive, by using their BU (Bangalore Urban) numbers which are generated by the BBMP (Bruhat Bengaluru Mahanagara Palike, the city's municipal corporation) after a patient is tested positive, and getting other patients admitted in their BU numbers. The going rate was ₹15,000 to ₹25,000 for ordinary nursing home beds, ₹30,000 to ₹40,000 for ICU beds and for non-ICU beds at so-called 2-star and 3-star hospitals, ₹50,000 to ₹75,000 for beds at well-managed missionary hospitals such as St. John's Medical College Hospital and Bangalore Baptist Hospital, and up to ₹100,000 (rupees one lakh) at so-called 5-star hospitals such as Apollo, BGS Gleneagles Global Hospital, and Manipal Hospital. The police suspected the duo to have contacts with the BBMP war room staff. Advocates Madhukara Maiya and Vinay Sreenivasa alleged on Twitter that Dr Regina Joseph, who was associated with setting up BBMP's war-room, was the (alleged) mastermind of the black-marketing racket. This whole racket was exposed by Tejasvi Surya, the Bangalore South BJP Member of Parliament.

On May 6, Faridabad Police arrested Congress sports cell officer Bijendra Mavi for his (alleged) involvement in black marketing of oxygen cylinders. Fifty cylinders (42 empty and 8 filled) were found in his vehicle.

On the same day, Delhi Police raided Nege Ju restaurant in Lodhi Colony and arrested the manager Hitesh Prakash plus three others. The next day, it raided two famous restaurants, Khan Chacha and Town Hall in Khan Market, the latter being a favourite of Sonia and Rahul Gandhi. A total of 524 oxygen concentrators were seized from four places.

The owner of all three restaurants in **Navneet Kalra**, who (allegedly) has close connections with senior Congress leaders (especially the 'first' son–in–law) as well as Arvind Kejriwal. In 2004–05, the Congress government nominated Kalra's name for a permanent 'nominated' membership to the prestigious Delhi Golf Club. When being sworn in as CM for the third time in February 2020, Kejriwal referred to Kalra as one of the 50 'shapers' (influencers) of Delhi.

AAP's Delhi minister Imran Hussain was caught hoarding 637 oxygen cylinders. Two associates of AAP MLA Amanatullah Khan were also arrested with large quantities of Remdesivir and oxygen cylinders. AAP was saying there are no vaccines for people, but was giving them to journalists, to get even more publicity, as if the hundreds of crores of taxpayer money he has spent on advertising himself (more about this later) was not sufficient.

Kalra also owns Mr Choy restaurant and Dayal Opticals at Khan Market, where he is said to own 30+ shops. The Khan Chacha chain, famous for its mutton and chicken rolls, has 16 outlets in Delhi and Gurugram. He has been featured in many Page-3 articles and photo-features, and has been seen partying with celebs such as cricketers Virat Kohli, MS Dhoni, Sachin Tendulkar, Rohit Sharma, Shikar Dhawan, Dinesh Karthik, Washington Sundar, Yuvraj Singh, Harbhajan Singh, and VVS Laxman; media baron (Times Group owner) Vineet Jain; actors Anushka Sharma, Rahul Dev, Angad Bedi, Sangeet Bijlani, and Geeta Basra; former Miss Universe Sushmita Sen; journalists Vir Sanghvi and Shampa Dhar-Kamath; amongst dozens of others. **We could not find a single tweet by any of them condemning Navneet Kalra for his co-vulturism.**

Why would they—after all, Kalra (allegedly) organised drug-fuelled parties for them in Delhi farmhouses. He also (allegedly) runs a high-profile escort (prostitution) racket in Delhi, as well as a cricket gambling enterprise.

On May 8, Delhi Police arrested **Gourav Khanna, CEO of Matrix Cellular**, which had imported the oxygen concentrators, of which the 524 were a part. The Delhi Police's initial probe and analysis of documents and invoices showed that 7,500 concentrators were procured (and most of them sold) by Kalra and Khanna. This would have fetched them a profit of ₹33.75 crores at a selling price of ₹70,000 and a landed cost of ₹25,000 each. The imports started in November 2020, which brings us to the question—was the second wave planned? More about this in a later chapter.

On the same day, Indore Police arrested Congress leader Yatindra Verma for allegedly selling oxygen flow metres and several other types of devices at 3-5 times their price.

Guess which lawyer is defending Navneet Kalra in court? It is none other than Congress leader and Rajya Sabha MP Dr Abhishek Manu Singhvi.

The PM CARES Fund had sent 10 ventilators to a Rajasthan Govt. hospital in Bharatpur (Rajasthan is ruled by the Congress). This government hospital told the media that the ventilators were not working. They were then lent to a private hospital where they miraculously started working and which was charging patients ₹35,000 per day for their use. In 20 days, ₹70 lakhs was made—how much of this was pocketed by Congress ministers and state government officials? We will never know, will we?

Rajesh Maheshwari, a local BJP leader in Ratlam, MP, was arrested for selling oxygen flow meters at inflated prices.

There are hundreds (maybe thousands) of such stories across India, but we don't want to fill more pages with this as you surely get the point. When the rich and powerful—who are friends of more rich and powerful and 'protected' by them—profit at such trying times, we can only bow our heads in shame!

Navneet & Kitty Kalra

Was the Second Wave Planned?

The second wave of COVID-19 gave the Congress party, its allies, AAP, TMC, and Akhilesh Yadav's Samajwadi Party a fresh (but best yet) chance to defame Prime Minister Narendra Modi and his government, with the help of willing partners in the AMB, especially the media.

Remember various events and issues like Dadri, protests over Rohith Vemula's death in a Hyderabad university (Rahul Gandhi, Arvind Kejriwal, and TMC leaders went there), Award Wapsi, the JNU protests after student leaders Kanhaiya Kumar and Umar Khalid were arrested for leading a mob shouting antinational slogans (attended again by Rahul and Kejriwal), the Bhima–Koregaon violence in Maharashtra, etc.? These were all probably orchestrated to defame Modi. Remember that senior Congress leader Mani Shankar Aiyar told a Pakistan TV channel (on his visit to our most friendly neighbour) that he needs their help to defeat Modi?

After the September 2016 surgical strikes carried out by the Indian Army in POK (Pakistan-occupied Kashmir), Rahul Gandhi accused Modi of doing "*Khoon in Dalali*", or brokering in soldiers' blood.

When Modi demonetized the old ₹500 and ₹1000 notes in November 2016, there was a ruckus created by opposition parties and the anti-Modi media about hundreds of people dying just by standing in queues outside banks to exchange their old notes with new ones. By December 8, the claim was that over 100 people had died. Firstly, people do not die because of standing in queues. People could have died of dehydration. Secondly, if some did die, why didn't they carry water bottles/thermoses, especially as the long queues had already been made by some 'famous vulture journalists' on TV? Thirdly, let's assume that 100 people did die in the said 21 days. At India's death rate of 26,109/ day in 2016, a total of 5,48,289 people would have died in those 21 days. 100 died due to queues? A hundred? Why didn't the opposition produce any evidence? We are not going to argue about the benefits of demonetization or the damage it caused to small and medium businesses in this book, as it is irrelevant. But the point is that **the opposition and the anti-Modi media were doing 'death politics' even then.**

You may remember the politics created after the GST Act was passed in the Parliament on March 29, 2017, and came into effect on July 1, 2017. GST has been a huge boon to the Indian economy. In an aggregate over the past 46 months, GST revenue has been more than 23% higher than what the 13 old taxes and cesses it replaced, would have been, at the same rate of growth of the economy.

After the February 2019 Balakot airstrikes in which the IAF bombed targets well inside Pakistan and inflicted 200-350 casualties, the Congress said that the Modi government had lied, that only trees were destroyed, and also inferred that the Indian Air Force chief had lied. All this was just to defame Modi.

During the 2019 election campaign, Rahul used the slogan "*Chowkidaar Chor Hai*" (the watchman is a thief) no less than 150 times, accusing Modi of taking bribes in the deal to purchase 36 Rafale multirole jets for the Indian Air Force from France. Having had six prime ministers preside over India for 54.4 years, the Congress cannot understand how an Indian PM can approve a ₹58,600 crore defence deal without a kickback.

But Modi came back with a bigger election victory in 2019, and became the first non-Congress prime minister to win a second term of five years after completing a full first term. A ruling party was returned to power with an absolute majority after 48 years, and with a bigger majority (than the previous elections) after 62 years.

The BJP-led NDA got 74% more votes than the Congress-led UPA. The Congress was decimated. It got 19.49% of the votes and just 52 out of 543 seats. Except in Tamil Nadu, the Congress got just seven seats in India's 10 largest states. It did not get a single seat in 17 states/UTs.

Therefore, the post-2019 plans to defame Modi had to be bigger!

It started with an uproar over the internet shutdown in Kashmir when the Modi government (in August 2019) got the President to issue an Order to revoke Articles 370 and 35A of the Constitution which had given a 'special status' to the erstwhile state of Jammu & Kashmir (J&K), and got a Bill passed in Parliament to divide J&K into two Union Territories (UTs), the UT of J&K, and the UT of Ladakh. This Bill was passed with a 67.2% majority in the Rajya Sabha and a 84.1% majority in the Lok Sabha. Even opposition parties such as Andhra Pradesh's ruling YSRCP and Odisha's ruling BJD supported it.

Congress leaders who supported the Modi government move included Jyotiraditya Scindia and Bhubaneswar Kalita (both are now with the BJP), RPN Singh, Milind Deora, Jitin Prasada, Deepender Hooda, Ranjeet Ranjan, and Jaiveer Shergill. Even former *Sadr-i-Riyasat* (President) of J&K Dr Karan Singh supported the move. In an *India Today* poll, 68.7% of people supported the move.

Yet, the Congress and their likeminded parties opposed it, either just for the sake of opposing Modi, or for appeasing the huge Muslim vote bank, or both.

Then came the protests against the CAA (Citizenship Amendment Act) and the NRC (National Register of Citizens) in December 2019 but this did not last more than three and a half months. However, 'planned and organised' communal clashes between supporters and opponents of CAA in Northeast Delhi led to at least 53 deaths. The same Umar Khalid of JNU fame was arrested for his alleged involvement. Former AAP councillor Tahir Hussain confessed about his role in the Northeast Delhi violence and admitted that he incited people to unleash violence. Hussain said that he met Khalid at an office of the extremist Islamic organisation PFI (Popular Front of India) in Shaheen Bagh on January 8, 2020. According to Delhi Police, Hussain's task was to collect as many glass bottles, petrol, acid, and stones as possible, on the roof of his house.

The PFI allegedly provided ₹120 crores for the Northeast Delhi riots. After every round of communal trouble or the busting of a terror module nowadays, PFI's name crops up. Rahul Gandhi met with the family of arrested Kerala journalist Siddique Kappan, who is alleged to have links with the PFI. When the PFI was fighting a legal case in 2019, it employed senior Congress leader Kapil Sibal for ₹77 lakhs as its lawyer.

In December 2019, Bollywood actor/director Farhan Akhtar invited the public to gather at the August Kranti Maidan in Mumbai to protest against the CAA, through a tweet. The distorted map of India displayed by Akhtar on his Twitter account carried the logo of "Stand With Kashmir" (**SWK**), an affiliate of the "Islamic Circle of North America" (**ICNA**). ICNA is linked with "Jamaat-E-Islami" (**JEI**), a banned organization in India. ICNA's sister organization is Muslim American Society (MAS), a designated terror organization in the UAE. ICNA has invited some 'honourable' speakers to its seminars, including **Al-Qaeda terrorist Anwar al-Awlaki** (killed by a US drone strike 21 days after the 9/11 terrorist attacks on New York City and Washington, D.C.), and **Pakistani ISI agent Ghulam Nabi Fai** (who was in jail in the US for 16 months). Jim Banks, a member of the lower house of the US Congress (their Parliament) has said that JEI promotes terrorism and radicalism in the Indian subcontinent. American lawyer and former US Congress staffer Cliff Smith wrote in June 2020 that US franchises of JEI, mainly ICNA and SWK have been damaging India by downplaying their affiliations with jihadis and seeking to help the Islamist cause. They hired the high-powered law firm Perkins Coie to misinform the US Congress about potential terror finance flowing from the US to the Kashmir region. Perkins Coie had defended various terror-linked suspects such as **Osama Bin-Laden's** driver and bodyguard, Salim Hamdan.

During the first wave of COVID-19 in 2020, the Congress-led AMB tried for a mass exodus of migrant workers from Mumbai, Delhi, Bengaluru, Chennai, Hyderabad, Pune, and other large cities to UP, Bihar, and other states, including Northeast states. However, this by and large failed.

In fact, **Modi's 'approval rating' was at an all-time high of 83-84% during the 51-day national lockdown** (83% during April 18-21, 2020, and 84% on May 2-3). An approval rating for a country's chief executive indicates his/her popularity and therefore the percentage of people who are likely to vote for him/her if elections were held that day. Modi's approval rating graph from August 6, 2019, to May 11, 2021, is given at the end of this chapter.

Simultaneously, **China's People Liberation Army (PLA)**, which has a 'secret' agreement with the dynasty's Rajiv Gandhi Foundation, which we shall cover in another chapter, and which had **started intruding into Eastern Ladakh, attacked the Indian Army, which led to violent clashes in the Galwan Valley**. But our brave soldiers, obviously under command of the diehard officers, thwarted the Chinese attempts. There is an unanswered question whether **Rahul Gandhi met a PLA General in Thailand in July 2020**—in the middle of the Indo-China faceoff in Ladakh. Is he willing to answer (and prove) that he did not?

When all of these tricks and plans failed, a brilliant new idea was strategized and executed—**the farmer agitation**. After all, farmers represent the largest vote bank in the country. This started in early August 2020 and is still going on, but is not getting enough publicity any more even from the anti-Modi media, due to the second wave. We have no way to confirm this, but it has been widely reported that Kejriwal and Congress's Punjab government even organised Khalistani separatists in this movement.

We are not going to comment about the benefits of the Modi government's farm reforms (against which the protests are happening) here as you can read about it in Amit Bagaria's book *Congress–Mukt Bharat*.

Amardeep Singh is the Co-founder of the US-based NGO "Sikh Coalition". It's website states that it is a community-based organization that works towards the realization of civil and human rights for all people. Since 2014, Singh has been working with economic terrorist George Soros's "Open Society Foundations" (**OSF**) as a Senior Program Officer. This is after he moved out from Sikh Coalition in September 2014, though he continues to remain its Co-founder. Amardeep Singh and Sikh Coalition are playing a prominent role in the US in raising support for the farmers' protests in India. *The New York Times* carried an advertisement paid for by "Justice for Migrant Women" and signed by 76 organizations claiming to be concerned farmers, activists, and citizens of the world. In the list of 'farmers, activists and citizens of the world' is the questionable organization "Council of American–Islamic Relations" (**CAIR**).

CAIR along with ICNA have been strong backers to the SWK global advocacy, which included billboard advertisements in the US. The aim of CAIR and ICNA is to attack the GOI's decision on Abrogation of Article 370 and to create global awareness on the so-called 'atrocities to Muslims in Kashmir by the GOI through Indian Armed Forces'. CAIR receives most of its funding from Qatar and Turkey. Turkey was one of the very few Muslim countries that opposed the decision of the Abrogation of Article 370 and threw its weight behind Pakistan on the issue. CAIR was included in the list of groups identified as the "Palestine Committee", created by the Muslim Brotherhood, and charged with supporting the terrorist group Hamas financially and politically in the US, as per InvestigateProject.org. Just as an example, in 2017 alone CAIR received $366,010 from OSF. OSF has worked with CAIR and its different branches in the US.

So, the moot question is: Did the Congress and its supporters and allies collaborate with any of these forces, either during the anti-CAA protests, or the farmer protests?

The COVID-19 second wave gave the Congress and other 'Leftists' an unprecedented opportunity.

Navneet Kalra and his partners imported 7,500 oxygen concentrators starting in November 2020 to black market them and make a profit of nearly ₹34 crores. You have already read about his political 'connections' in the previous chapter.

Why in November? COVID-19 cases in November averaged 42,662 per day, compared with 60,424 per day in October, and 87,411 per day in September. So the first wave was clearly on a steady decline. And even in the peak during September, did you see thousands of tweets or hundreds of WhatsApp messages or scores of media articles / TV shows about an oxygen shortage?

Were they planning for a second wave? Did they know about it well in advance?

Rahul went to Europe and Sonia went to the US in December 2020. Why? To meet with people who could fund another unrest in India, such as the 'think-tanks' secretly funded by the CIA? You can read all about this in Amit Bagaria's sensational book *USAma—Is USA the World's Largest Terrorist?*

Of course the Congress party's standard excuse will be that Rahul went to meet his ailing *nani* (mother's mother) in Italy and Sonia went for a regular medical check-up.

On February 6, 2021, **Congress announced that it will recruit five lakh Social Media (SM) warriors** for their IT Cell, to counter the BJP IT Cell. Five lakh people for SM? That's more than 8.5 times that Facebook has. As far as we know, the BJP IT Cell only has about 15,000 workers and volunteers. So why did Congress need more than 33 times that number? **And more importantly, why in February 2021? Thirty-two days before the second wave started.** Sufficient time for recruitment and training?

Digressing from the topic for a second, can't this huge army of five lakh 'paid volunteers' do a better job in helping fight the pandemic, than helping fight the BJP on social media?

We know what they are doing. Rahul with 1.85 crore followers on Twitter gets up to 29,700 retweets (including quote tweets) and up to 1.043 lakh likes, compared with Prime Minister Modi who has 6.81 crore followers (3.68x of Rahul), but only gets maximum 1.14x of Rahul's retweets and 1.69x of Rahul's likes. This is not only due to tens of lakhs of fake accounts created by the paid volunteers (yes, BJP does it too, but on a much smaller scale!), but also by spending money. Yes, anything on Twitter can be bought. The same is true of other social media (SM) platforms like Facebook, Instagram, and YouTube.

Where did the second wave start? In Congress + allies-ruled **Maharashtra**! Which state had 53% of all COVID-19 cases and 45.3% of all deaths in India in the 40-day period from March 1 to April 30, 2021?? **Maharashtra**, which has less than 9% of India's population!! Who created the first panic about shortage of hospital beds, oxygen, and drugs like Remdesivir??? **Maharashtra** again!!! Which state has 21.2% of the cumulative cases and 29.4% of cumulative deaths???? **Maharashtra**!!!!

Which four states have the highest number of cases per lakh? All are opposition-ruled states, and two have Congress governments. Which four states have the highest deaths per lakh? Again, all are opposition-ruled states, and three have Congress governments.

But who is everyone blaming? No, not Maharashtra or the other opposition-ruled states, but Narendra Modi!!!

Why is Modi being blamed when health is a state subject (not a Central subject) and the management of the COVID-19 pandemic was given to the states in 2020 because they aggressively demanded it?

Oxygen concentrators/cylinders and medicines like Remdesivir were stocked by the AMB well in advance, so that ordinary citizens would not get these when the need arose. We wouldn't be even a little surprised if hospital beds were filled up by people who didn't need hospitalization. We also wouldn't be surprised if crooked owners of over 70% of private hospitals were made partners in the crime. *(Amit Bagaria was India's No. 1 hospital development consultant for five years, so he says this with full knowledge).*

A majority of the SOS messages on SM platforms for hospital beds, oxygen and oxygen concentrators, Remdesivir, Tocilizumab, etc., are from the fake SM handles, most of them probably created by the five lakh 'paid volunteers' of the Congress SM team.

They are then retweeted or reposted by real people with tens of thousands or lakhs of followers, so that the panic could be spread as wide as possible. We have seen hundreds of such tweets from Robert Vadra's brother-in-law Tehseen Poonawalla. We don't know how many are genuine but can definitely make an educated guess.

In some cases, dozens (maybe more) of SOS messages have all the same details (such as Blood Group, Age, etc.) about a patient except his or her name. In some cases, people who have copied the post haven't even changed the name.

Remdesivir was made to sound like a wonder drug, despite the WHO saying back in November 2020 that it recommends against the use of Remdesivir in COVID-19 patients (more on that later).

Here are just three examples of completely fake tweets. There were lakhs since March 1, 2021, and we have more than 150, but can't fit them all here. Besides, you will go crazy reading all of them.

We know the six tweets on the left are not readable, but they have the exact same message in Hindi: "3 *ghante tak lagatar tadapne ke baad meri maa mujhe chodkar chali gai* @narendramodi *aapka system jeet gaya mera pariwaar haar* gaya" which translates to "*After panting for three hours, my mother left me and died. Narendra Modi, your system won, my family lost.*"

The guy on the top replaced his mom with his girlfriend. The second @dhruvmukhes retweets random tweets about IPL and against all political parties. He probably did it for the ₹20/- **Yes, Rupees Twenty is what they earn from political parties.** @RanjitKumarMai6 and @SASWATIPAUL4 are ardent Mamata Banerjee supporters. The fifth @40p8bvF5U6IdQFH (who names a Twitter account like this?) claims to be a Zila Panchayat vice president in Ayodhya. The sixth account @ShoaibRyalty doesn't exist anymore. There were 100+ of the same tweets. **Some attached pics of their 'common' dead mother while others didn't.** Some used anti-Modi hashtags such as #ModiHataoDeshBachao, #ModiResignOrRepeal, and #ShameOnModi while others didn't.

Not only did the second 'pair' both lose their *nana* (mother's father) in the exact same way, they also tweeted the exact same message. Swati Maliwal is the Chairperson of the Delhi Commission for Women and is very close to Arvind Kejriwal. We don't know whether she actually lost her *nana* or not, but if she did, she has our heartfelt condolences.

Since Kalpna's tweet was 47 minutes later, it was obviously a fake. The account @kaplnameena01 doesn't exist anymore, so was obviously created for mischief. Her actual account (pic second from bottom right) says she is a journalist, but we could not find any articles by her on Google despite going to the fourth page. She also claims to be Ex. INC (Congress) President Student of "lows" (whatever that means), and an engineering student. Can she at least decide what she really is?

The tweet on the top right actually gave us a laugh! Which Muslim puts a saffron garland on the photo of their dead father?

Since the hashtags were trended by the Congress party, it is obvious who paid them.

Congress trends 6-10 such anti-Modi hashtags per week and, based on the average number of tweets in each trended hashtag, we estimate the Twitter marketing cost at ₹2.4 crores per month. Add an estimated ₹3.6 crores for Facebook, Instagram, and YouTube. Add about ₹1.5 crores for 'paid news" articles. The wages of 4.95 lakh 'volunteers' @ ₹5000 and the salary of 5,000 supervisors @ ₹40,000 comes to ₹268 crores.

Is the Congress party spending Rs 280 crores a month to malign the Prime Minister on the world stage, and therefore MALIGNING INDIA ITSELF?

With office rentals and other costs, we are talking about a **total expense of minimum ₹280 crores per month to malign the PM, and therefore the country, globally.**

Almost the same thing happened with poor Donald Trump in the US. Panic about COVID-19 was created so that he lost the elections. Once Joe Biden came to power, most of the noise stopped, as if COVID-19 had ended there.

The reality is very different. The US reported 46,239 average daily cases during Trump's presidency; it has reported 1,20,113 average daily cases between November 24, 2020, when Trump conceded defeat, and power virtually came into the hands of Biden's 'transition' team, and May 31, 2021. Yes, the US has had 2.6 times more daily cases under Biden than under Trump.

Trump was against the 'pharma lobby', so no vaccines came out when he was president. Within 19 days of Trump conceding to Biden, vaccines started getting delivered. The pharma lobby contributed $100 million (₹740 crores) to Biden's presidential 'Inauguration' program, which is a set of ceremonies when a new POTUS is officially sworn in on January 20 of every Olympics' year (2020, 2016, 2012, etc.).

Coming back to India, yes it is true that we had 1.327 crore cases from Mar 16 to May 15, 2021. The cases in just these 61 days were 1.163 times the cases we had in the 13 previous months. We also sadly had 1,11,427 deaths in this period. But given our population, these numbers were small when you compare them to 15-20 other countries with a population of more than four crores. We shall give all the comparisons in a later chapter.

The Congress and other Leftists' 'New Idea of India" was to create panic, to make people afraid that they wouldn't get a hospital bed, or oxygen, or Remdesivir, and tens of thousands of rich people started buying all this from the black market and stocking it at home, thus depriving not-so-rich people who actually needed it. This itself probably led to at least 50,000 deaths.

In their quest to oust Modi, the Congress and other Leftists did great damage to the country as well as its well-built reputation (over the last seven years) in the eyes of the world. How different are they from Xi Jinping who unleashed the deadly Coronavirus upon the world?

Modi has been able to unite Hindus ever since he became the PM in 2014, and even more so with the Ayodhya Ram Mandir construction starting soon, as well as the revocation of Article 370.

Therefore, **the only way for Congress to try and oust Modi is to divide Hindus once again, just like the Mughals and the British did!**

And what better way than to have pictures of Hindu *shamshan ghats* (cremation grounds) plastered on front pages of the world's leading newspapers and shown on major international TV channels?

The foreign media does this because: (1) They are paid by their home country's governments (spy agencies) to malign India, as no country wants a third superpower after the US and China (not that anyone except China itself wants China), or (2) They are paid directly by entities such as the Congress party, or (3) The anti-Modi journalists (many of them Indian) who write the negative stories about India are paid, or (4) Media is always looking for sensational news stories (the first lesson taught in the Journalism 101 class at Amit's American university was that 'dog bites man' is not news, whereas 'man bites dog' is news); or a combination of two or more of these reasons.

What better way to make Hindus very angry than to malign the Kumbh Mela, to show that their PM doesn't care for their lives, that elections are more important for him? What better way than to show that the government doesn't care for farmers?

Before the UP elections in 2017, rumours were spread that Rahul Gandhi was going to marry a Brahmin girl, just to try and get some Hindu votes.

Fake accounts in the name of Hindu individuals or groups have been created on social media by the Congress-led AMB, and they abuse Modi and his government on a daily basis. This shows real Hindus that Modi is losing popularity, and they begin to doubt their own support for him. This is a classic CIA trick.

An advocate who has been appearing on TV debates regularly for several years and speaking in support of Modi and the BJP, recently said that he no longer supports Modi because two of his friends died of COVID-19. So the AMB seems to be achieving its objectives.

But we wouldn't be surprised if Narendra Modi springs a surprise on all of them soon, as he is much smarter than all the people in the Congress and the rest of the AMB put together.

As Ajay Devgn said in Singham: *"Kutton ka jhund kitna bhi bada ho... uske liye ek sher hi kaafi hota hai."* *("No matter how big a group of dogs is ... for them one tiger is more than enough.")*

The AMB will suffer grave consequences due to the sins they have committed against 139 crore Indians. It's called "Karma".

We have written this chapter because you must know the truth about India's Covid crisis, in fact, we must all know **THE TRUTH ABOUT INDIA'S COVID CRISIS.**

PS: *This chapter was published as an article penned by Amit Bagaria in* Goa Chronicle *and* News Bharati *on May 17. The next day, there was a leak of a Congress 'Toolkit' which pretty much exposed what he said the previous day. There were more than 3.4 lakh tweets with the hashtag #CongressToolkitExposed within six hours.*

The Congress claimed that the Toolkit was a fake, and that it had been created by the BJP.

Have a look at some of the some of the things in the alleged Toolkit, which we do not know is authentic or not. But we were not surprised at all to read any of this, though each and every one of these activities were definitely undertaken by the Congress and their Leftist supporters.

VI. Prime Minister Modi's image: The approval ratings of Prime Minister Modi have been high and have not dipped despite crisis and mismanagement. This is an opportunity to destroy his image and erode his popularity. Towards this end:

  a. Use resources created on social media to question Modi's incompetence from handles which look like Modi or BJP supporters.
  b. International media coverage by foreign correspondents in India can be tailored to exclusively focus on Modi and his mismanagement. Liaise with foreign journalists and Indian Oped writers in foreign publications and brief them on talking points.
  c. Use of dramatic pictures of funerals and dead bodies, which is already being done by foreign media. Such journalists can be facilitated by our local cadre in various districts to get the right image and then their reporting may be magnified.
  d. The envelope can be pushed to start using demeaning phrases for Modi in intellectual discourse by friendly intellectuals and opinion makers so that they have greater acceptability when used politically
  e. Use the phrase 'Indian strain' whenever talking of the new mutant. Social Media volunteers may call it 'Modi strain'.

VII. Others: A series of other actions can be taken to amplify the image of a clueless and insensitive BJP and to corner it on its mismanagement.
  a. Use phrases like 'Missing' Amit Shah, 'Quarantined' Jaishankar, 'Sidelined' Rajnath Singh, 'Insensitive' Nirmala Sitharaman, etc.
  b. Cover stories in weekly magazines which reinforce the same image of missing government can be encouraged in amenable publications.
  c. Letters to Modi to be written at regular intervals with suggestions that are a good mix of emotionally appealing ideas among some common-sense suggestions.

AICC Research Department   Page 4
This document is research input for the Indian National Congress and does not represent the official party line.

Someone forwarded a very appropriate WhatsApp message after the Toolkit was exposed: "सिर्फ वो ही गिने गए कोरोना में, जो मर गए शरीर से; उनकी गिनती अभी बाकी है, जो गिर गए ज़मीर से!!" The English translation is: "*Only those were counted in Corona, who lost their lives; the people who lost their conscience are yet to be counted!!*"

Yes, the Congress was right in saying that *"The approval ratings of Prime Minister Modi have been high and have not dipped …"* The ratings had hardly dipped even 46 days after the second wave began, 21 days after COVID-19 cases crossed one lakh per day for the first time, and six days after they crossed two lakhs per day.

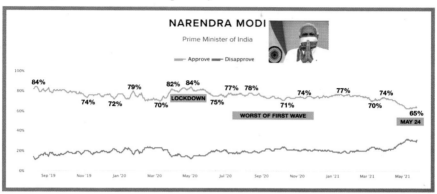

Based on the undeniable fact that the activities listed in the purported Toolkit started happening around May 1, we estimate that the alleged document was prepared around April 27-28, when Modi's approval rating was still 67%.

This tweet from an advisor to Congress/Gandhi family-owned newspaper *National Herald* also provides some evidence.

The farmer protests started after India fought the first wave successfully. They burned the cell towers of Reliance Jio. A Mumbai cop allegedly planted explosives outside Mukesh Ambani's house.

Congress and other AMB members advocated boycott of Indian vaccines. There was a fire at the plant of SII. There were fires at other pharma units. There was a huge second wave. SII's owner was threatened (supposedly by Maharashtra government ministers) and had to move to London temporarily.

All of these are coincidences???

Are the Pharma Industry & Hospitals anti-Modi?

Is it possible that the Indian and international pharma industry, as well as the Indian hospital sector, are against PM Modi? Here are some reasons we think that there is a strong possibility that this is true!

Almost 16 crore people (11.5% of India's population) have enrolled in the Pradhan Mantri Jan Arogya Yojana (PMJAY), the world's largest scheme of its kind. It provides up to ₹5 lakh per family per year for hospitalisation to the bottom 40% of the population. Almost 1.85 crore completely free hospital treatments have already been done. The 20,000+ hospitals providing services under this scheme get quite low (negotiated and contracted) prices from the GOI under the PMJAY.

Pradhan Mantri Bharatiya Janaushadhi Pariyojana provides quality medicines at affordable prices through *Janaushadhi Kendras*. Generic drugs, which are equivalent in quality and efficacy to expensive branded drugs, are available at lesser prices, which have seen up to 93% reduction. The price of anti-rabies injections has been reduced by 52.3%. More than 7,770 *kendras* have already been opened.

In addition, the Modi government have made manufacturers reduce prices of medical appliances, devices and consumables such as life-saving stents used in angioplasty to ensure blood supply to and from the heart, have been slashed by up to 80%.

Obviously, the profits that pharma companies and hospitals were earning before Modi came to power have been greatly affected, and they cannot be happy with him.

Even the insurance industry's profits have been affected. More than 10.32 crore citizens have enrolled in the Pradhan Mantri Jeevan Jyoti

Bima Yojana, which provides life insurance cover of ₹2 lakh at a premium of just ₹330 per annum. About 23.36 crore citizens have enrolled in the Pradhan Mantri Suraksha Bima Yojana which provides accident insurance cover of ₹2 lakh at a premium of just ₹12 per annum.

Comparison with Other Countries

Let's get back to some important data points. Yes, India reported a whopping **4,14,182 COVID-19 cases on May 6, 2021, and crossed 4,00,000 (four lakh) cases on three out of seven days** during the week. But how do India's cases in this very difficult period compare with other relatively large countries which have reported a very high number of cases in any given week?

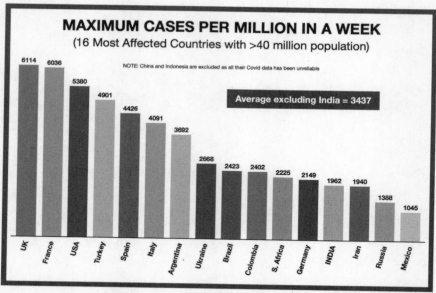

MAXIMUM CASES PER MILLION IN A WEEK
(16 Most Affected Countries with >40 million population)

NOTE: China and Indonesia are excluded as all their Covid data has been unreliable

Average excluding India = 3437

UK	France	USA	Turkey	Spain	Italy	Argentina	Ukraine	Brazil	Colombia	S. Africa	Germany	INDIA	Iran	Russia	Mexico
6114	6036	5380	4901	4426	4091	3692	2668	2423	2402	2225	2149	1962	1940	1388	1045

As you can see from the chart, despite India reporting more than 2.73 million (27.3 lakh) cases in a week (April 30 to May 6, 2021, including both days), we were much lower than seven out of 15 other countries with minimum population of 40 million (four crore) and comfortably lower than three others, when we look at cases per million. In fact, the average for the 15 countries excluding India has been 491 cases per million per day, compared to 280.3 for India.

The logic for using countries with minimum 40 million people is quite simple. There are only 14 countries with over 100 million (10 crore) people, and eight (China, Indonesia, Pakistan, Nigeria, Bangladesh, Japan, Ethiopia, and Egypt) are underreporting numbers, mismanaging testing/reporting, or have miraculous immunity from COVID-19. That leaves six countries, which is too small a sample to make comparisons. If we picked another 15 countries with over 50 million people, seven (Vietnam, Democratic Republic of Congo [DRC], Thailand, Tanzania, Kenya, Myanmar, and South Korea) have the same issue/s. By picking countries with a minimum population of 40 million, we were able to have a minimum of 15 countries in the comparison charts.

Even if you believe that India's actual case (and death) count is larger than 'official' figures, how do we know that the same is not the case with many other countries? In fact, going by the nature of governments in Turkey, Ukraine, Colombia, Iran, and Russia, it is very likely that they have fudged data and their numbers are much higher. More about this later.

How does India compare with other countries in the cumulative number of cases? These are not specific to the second wave, but a combined total of all 'reported' cases in the respective countries.

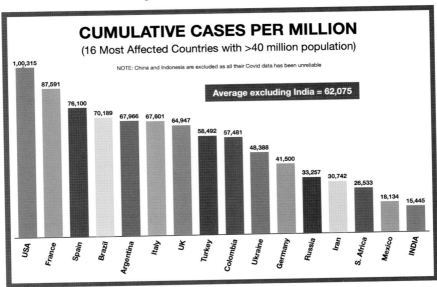

In this chart, all the 15 other countries have higher cumulative cases than India as on May 6, 2021. And the differences with India (except in the case of Mexico) are huge. India's number is just 24.9% of the average. Does that not mean that India has done far better than all other relatively large countries?

The population of 48 European countries (including Russia), the US, Brazil, and Mexico, is roughly equal to 1.024 times India's population, and they had 2.39 times India's cases.

The graph below shows an excellent comparison of how India fared compared to the five other countries with the most number of cumulative cases (more than 50 lakh cases).

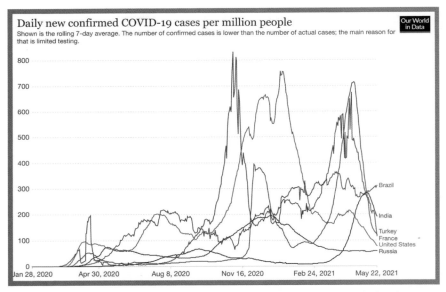

As you can see, **even in the second wave peak which looks very severe due to the sheer numbers when you don't compare them to our population**, we have fared better than all of the other five countries when you do compare them to the population, which—we repeat to emphasize the point—is the only correct way to do these comparisons.

Now let us compare how much each of these countries spends on healthcare PER PERSON compared to India, and how many cumulative cases they have reported compared to India.

The US, which spends ~38.63 times more on healthcare per person on healthcare than India, has reported ~6.86 times more cumulative cases per million than India from the beginning of the pandemic. The figures for all the 17 countries are given in the Table below. Please look at the last two columns. How you decipher this is up to you, but we firmly believe that one cannot compare India's COVID-19 management capabilities with countries that spend 2.5 to 38.6 times on healthcare PER PERSON each year.

Country	Cases per Million People	Healthcare Expenditure per person in US$	Health Exp. per person (Multiple of India)	Cases per Million (Multiple of India)
USA	1,00,315	10,624	38.6	6.5
Germany	41,500	6,098	22.2	2.7
France	87,591	5,250	19.1	5.7
UK	64,947	4,620	16.8	4.2
Italy	67,601	3,624	13.2	4.4
Spain	76,100	3,576	13.0	4.9
Argentina	67,966	1,990	7.2	4.4
Iran	30,742	1,691	6.1	2.0
Brazil	70,189	1,531	5.6	4.5
Russia	33,257	1,488	5.4	2.2
Turkey	58,492	1,171	4.3	3.8
Colombia	57,481	1,155	4.2	3.7
S. Africa	26,533	1,129	4.1	1.7
Mexico	18,134	1,066	3.9	1.2
Ukraine	48,388	683	2.5	3.1
INDIA	15,445	275	1.0	1.0

There is another comparison that we should do. The US borrows much more money (and also prints more for spending) as compared with other countries.

As per IMF data of 2018, the US's gross national debt was 11.6 times that of India. The Table with figures of the top 15 countries by their gross national debt is given in the next page. Of course it is easy for the US to spend 38.6 times more than India on healthcare when it's debt is 11.6 times higher.

It is a different matter that **we should be spending much more on healthcare** (*Amit Bagaria used to say this frequently in several talks and media interviews when his company was India's No.1 hospital / healthcare infrastructure development consultancy from 1998 to 2002*) but India has to be a much richer economy to achieve this.

Rank ⇕	Country	⇕	Debt to GDP	⇕	Gross Debt ($B)	⇕	% of World
#1	United States		104.3%		$21,465		31.0%
#2	Japan		237.1%		$11,788		17.0%
#3	China, People's Republic of		50.6%		$6,764		9.8%
#4	Italy		132.2%		$2,744		4.0%
#5	France		98.4%		$2,736		3.9%
#6	United Kingdom		86.8%		$2,455		3.5%
#7	Germany		61.7%		$2,438		3.5%
#8	India		68.1%		$1,851		2.7%
#9	Brazil		87.9%		$1,642		2.4%
#10	Canada		89.9%		$1,540		2.2%
#11	Spain		97.1%		$1,386		2.0%
#12	Mexico		53.6%		$655		0.9%
#13	Korea, Republic of		37.9%		$652		0.9%
#14	Australia		41.4%		$588		0.8%
#15	Belgium		102.0%		$543		0.8%

All of the blame for not being a richer economy cannot go to a man (Modi) who has been PM for seven out of 73.75 years (9.5% of the time), or to a party (the BJP) that has been in power for 13.2 years (17.9% of the time). The Congress party has ruled India directly or indirectly for 57.3 years, or 77.7% of the time.

As per World Bank data (http://bit.ly/India_PCGDP), India's Per Capita GDP (PCGDP) grew from US$82.19 in 1960 to $413.3 in 1998, at a compounded annual growth rate of only 4.34%. This was a 38-year-long period during which Congress or Congress-supported governments were in power for 91.4% of the time. The foundation for a higher growth rate should have been laid during this period, especially immediately after Deng Xiaoping in 1978 started opening up China to attract foreign investment, which led to unprecedented growth in the Chinese economy. Today, it is laughable to even compare India to China on any economic parameter.

In her 2012 book *Indira Gandhi: Tryst With Power* Indira's cousin Nayantara Sahgal wrote that India lost 10 years of development due to Indira's policies. In his 2019 book *The Promise of India* the senior diplomat and economist Dr Jaimini Bhagwati wrote that, had it not been for Indira Gandhi's restrictive economic policies, the reforms of the early 1990s could have been carried out in the 1970s, and India's economy would have been close to $10 trillion (₹740 lakh crore) by 2018.

Let us not forget that **the world had acknowledged that India had far fewer COVID-19 cases (per million or per lakh) than most other countries during the first wave** mainly because Modi took the decision of an early national lockdown, when India had only 536 total reported COVID-19 cases, and the maximum cases reported in a single day was only 103. And this lockdown was extended three times, to make it a total of 51 days, one of the longest continuous lockdowns anywhere in the world. No such measure had been taken by Dr Manmohan Singh in 2009-10 despite India having ~45,000 reported H1Ni Swine Flu cases and 2,725 deaths. (*Amit's father's younger brother lost his life to Swine Flu.*)

It is also very important to look at the cumulative case count in the context of the total number of tests conducted. This is because, the fewer the number of tests done, the fewer will be the number of positive cases reported (for any disease), and vice-versa.

It is therefore not surprising that the DRC has reported a very low number of cases per million, as they have only done 16.54 tests per 100 million (10 crore) people as on May 7, 2021. Here are some other relatively large countries (population over 50 million or five crore) which have all done very low testing and therefore have low case numbers.

COUNTRY	Population in Million	TESTS / 100 Million	CASES / Million
Nigeria	210.44	92.15	786
Ethiopia	117.36	222.38	2,229
Egypt	103.96	261.17	2,262
Vietnam	98.08	301.60	33
Kenya	54.77	312.29	2,970
Bangladesh	166.08	338.03	4,649
Myanmar	54.72	472.87	2,612
Pakistan	224.51	541.17	3,805
Indonesia	275.97	549.83	6,195
Japan	126.15	979.28	4,967

The numbers (as on May 4) for the total number of tests done per 100 million people in 20 large countries with a minimum population of 50 million people are given in the next chart. If you multiply by 100, you get the rough number of tests done per million (10 lakh) people.

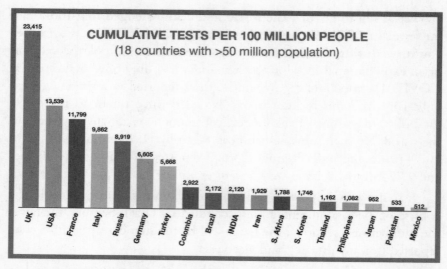

While India has fared much better in its testing numbers than far richer countries such as Japan, South Korea, Iran, Mexico, Thailand, South Africa, and Indonesia, we could have still done better. (*Amit had emphasized this in over 200 blog posts that he had written on the COVID-19 pandemic between March and November 2020, which you can find at www.bagariaamit.com.*)

Instead of 2120 tests per 100 million people, India could have easily tested 1.5 times that number. If that were the case, and if the TPR (number tested positive out of the total number tested) were the same for the additional 14.74 crore tests (India had conducted 29.48 crore tests as on May 4, 2021), we may have had reported a total of ~3.1 crore cumulative cases, very close to the US's ~3.3 crore, the highest in the world. Between March 13 and June 6, 2021, India's average COVID-19 tests per day have gone up to 16,33,661, from just 6,18,738 per day in one year before that, an increase of 2.64 times. Why couldn't we do this earlier?

As on May 4, the world (excluding China) had done ~2.053 billion (~205.28 crore) tests, and India's share was 14.37% compared to its share of 21.67% of the world population (excluding China). Therefore, India's testing share was 66.31% of its population share, and if we had conducted 3180 tests per 100 million instead of 2120, we would have been at par with our population share.

Anyway, 2120 is not that bad, considering that India's Per Capita GDP (PCGDP) of $2191 is much lower than the nine other countries that have done more testing per million (Source: International Monetary Fund's April 2021 World Economic Outlook Database).

COUNTRY	Testing as multiple of India (A)	PCGDP as multiple of India (B)	A/B
Germany	3.12	23.7	13.2%
USA	6.39	31.2	20.5%
France	5.56	20.5	27.1%
Italy	4.65	16.0	29.1%
Brazil	1.02	3.2	31.9%
UK	11.04	21.2	52.1%
Colombia	1.38	2.63	52.5%
Turkey	2.67	4.26	62.7%
Russia	4.21	5.3	84.9%

Except Russia, all the other countries have done far lesser testing than India, when we compare their economies.

Also, the fact that India has done more testing per 100 million people than Japan (~5.87x higher per capita income than India based on purchasing power parity), South Korea (~5.42x), Iran (~2.91x), Mexico (~2.6x), Thailand (~2.5x), South Africa (~1.89x), and Indonesia (~1.72x), is a feat in itself, and the GOI, plus those state governments that did higher testing than the national ratio (which we shall compare in the next chapter) must be congratulated for that, notwithstanding the fact that they could have done better.

While we are looking at these numbers, it is also quite important to study the data pertaining to the TPR in different countries and regions around the world. The TPRs (as on May 4) for 20 large countries with a minimum population of 50 million (five crore) people are given in the next chart. The only reason we have included Japan, Indonesia, the Philippines, Thailand, Pakistan, and Bangladesh in this chart is to give a comparison with other large Asian countries including India's neighbours.

The average TPR for 209 countries excluding China is not much different from the average of these 20 large countries. **India's TPR of 7% is below the world average.** Though it was ~8% and had peaked at 15.7% during the first wave, it plateaued to ~2% between December 2020 and February 2021, but **made a huge jump to an average of 17.16% between April 5 and May 4, 2021, with a peak of 25.3% on April 25.** This is again something that could not have been anticipated, as less than 10% of all countries have experienced such an increase in TPR between their peaks.

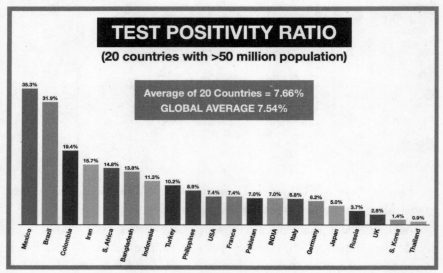

Central & South America (or Latin America), including Mexico, has the highest TPR of average ~23.42% for 49 countries/territories. This is followed by Africa, with an average TPR of ~10.41% for 54 countries (excluding Tanzania, Comoros, and Western Sahara as they do not report testing data). The US and Canada combined have an average TPR of ~7.21%.

The 47 countries of Asia (excluding China and Tajikistan) have an average TPR of ~6.4%. However, an interesting phenomenon is that 18 countries in the Middle East have a TPR of ~7.49%. It is ~5.9% in eight South-East Asian countries, and ~3.31% in Japan, South Korea, and Taiwan. While Taiwan could be fudging numbers (after all, it is China's younger cousin), is South Korea also doing the same, considering that it is a US ally and a very well-developed nation?

Europe (including the UK) has a TPR of ~5.97%.

Considering all of the above data, contrary to #FakeNews and rumours spread by those who have their own reasons to do it, it can be safely assumed that, overall, barring some possible exceptions that we will cover in the next chapter, India has not fudged its TPR, meaning that government labs have not converted COVID-19 positive test results into negative based on instructions from ruling parties in different states. If state governments had done this, the 'news' could have easily been leaked to the media by people who work at these labs. If there were any such reports, in our memory, they were only from West Bengal. We will do a state-wise study in the next chapter.

Let us look at two more comparisons. The first is the Deaths per Million as of May 6, 2021.

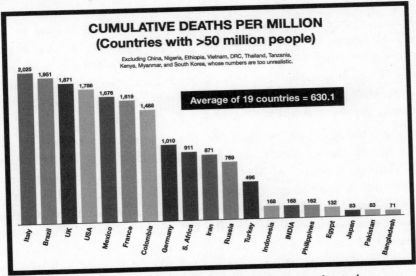

Yes, the number of COVID-related deaths in India is low, at only 26.66% of the average of these 19 countries. There could be two explanations for this.

The first is that India has a much younger population compared to Western countries. India's median age as per the CIA World Factbook is 28.7 years, compared with Italy's 46.5, the UK's 40.6, the US's 38.5, France's 41.7, Germany's 47.8, Russia's 40.3, and Turkey's 32.2 years. Indonesia at a median age of 31.1, the Philippines at 24.1, and Egypt also at 24.1 have a similar death rate as India. The only outliers are the Latin American countries Brazil (33.2 years), Mexico (29.3), Colombia (31.2); and South Africa (28); but as we saw before, these two regions/continents are the worst affected by COVID-19.

We are quite surprised that a country like Japan (median age 48.6, second-highest in the world) has such low death numbers despite their very high urbanization and population density. But as anyone who has been to Japan will testify, a large percentage of the population there wears face masks even in normal course, and professionals who encounter a lot of other people in their daily jobs (such as taxi drivers, bus drivers, porters, etc.) also wear gloves. As far as the low numbers in Pakistan and Bangladesh are concerned, the less said the better.

The second reason could be that deaths have been underreported across India, and if this is indeed the case, it could be either because the governments (Central and states) want to suppress the numbers, or because of sheer mismanagement. Even if the actual deaths are 3x the 'official' figures, we would be at 80% of the world average. And that is without factoring the very real possibility that deaths have been quite possibly underreported by Iran, Turkey, Indonesia, the Philippines, Egypt, Pakistan, and Bangladesh, and quite possibly by Japan also, given the very low number there.

And we may just be right. As per an analysis published by the Institute of Health Metrics and Evaluation (IHME) at the University of Washington School of Medicine on May 6, COVID-19 had caused ~6.9 million deaths, more than double what official numbers show. **IHME found that Covid deaths were significantly underreported in almost every country, including the US**, whose media has been severely critical of India. Latin America, Central Europe, Eastern Europe, and Central Asia are hardest hit in terms of deaths. This figure only includes deaths caused directly by the SARS-CoV-2 virus (popularly called the 'Coronavirus'), not deaths caused by the pandemic's disruption to health care systems and communities.

In the US, official deaths reported were 574,043 but IHME put the actual deaths at a shocking 905,289 (2,722 per million). In India official numbers were 221,181 but IHME puts the number at 654,395 (470 per million, or just 17.3% of the US).

Yes, developed countries including the US, Japan, Russia, Germany, Spain, Italy, the UK, and France have all underreported deaths. Here is the IHME data for the top 20 countries affected by COVID-19.

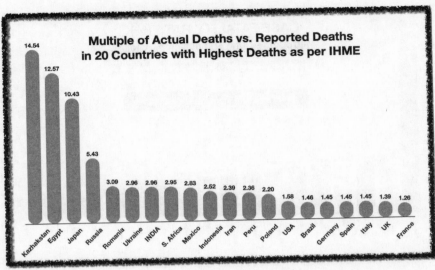

Interestingly, the IHME report does not feature the origin of the COVID-19 pandemic—China. That's because there is no report anywhere on the actual deaths in China, which officially claims only 4,636 deaths, or only 3.22 per million, compared to the 416.8, global average, which goes up to ~917 as per the IHME study. China's 'official' deaths are just 0.77% of the world's official death figures.

If we were to assume that India's actual number is 2.96 times the official number and the world's actual number is 2.15 times the reported deaths (as per IHME), it means India's cumulative deaths per million was ~497 on May 6, and the global average was ~896—therefore, **India's death rate is ~55.5% of the world's death rate, despite our poor healthcare infrastructure.**

"Many countries have devoted exceptional effort to measuring the pandemic's toll, but our analysis shows how difficult it is to accurately track a new and rapidly spreading infectious disease," said Dr Chris Murray, IHME's director.

However, before coming to a conclusion, let us look at the Case Fatality Rate (CFR), or the percentage of positive COVID-19 cases which have resulted in deaths. This is perhaps more important than the death rate chart, as the death rate by itself (without factoring total cases) means very little.

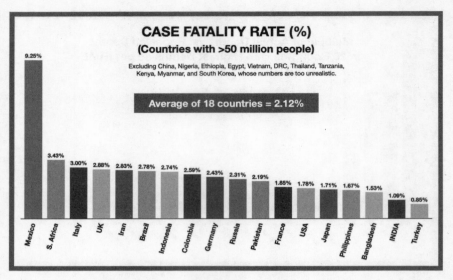

CASE FATALITY RATE (%)
(Countries with >50 million people)

Excluding China, Nigeria, Ethiopia, Egypt, Vietnam, DRC, Thailand, Tanzania, Kenya, Myanmar, and South Korea, whose numbers are too unrealistic.

Average of 18 countries = 2.12%

If we exclude Mexico (which seems to be a very odd outlier) from this chart, the average of the balance 17 countries falls to 1.96%. Even then, India's 1.09% seems to be very low, despite the fact that India has a lower median age, as we have said before.

Therefore, **it can be safely concluded that death rates in India are being underreported.**

A *Times of India* front page article in Bengaluru said that data collected by them showed that 3,104 Covid-protocol cremations were done in the city between March 1 and April 26, 2021, whereas official government data had the figure at 1,422 deaths. This means that actual deaths were 2.18 times the official figure.

If we estimate that the actual number of deaths in India are triple the official figures, our CFR goes up to 3.27%, which is very believable, considering that India's health infrastructure is not as good as most of the other countries in the above chart, and that the IHME report says that almost all countries have underreported deaths.

This is what the above chart looks like after factoring in the IHME study. It has only 13 countries as the IHME report does not cover Colombia, Pakistan, the Philippines, Bangladesh, and Turkey, whose underreporting must be even beyond IHME's imagination.

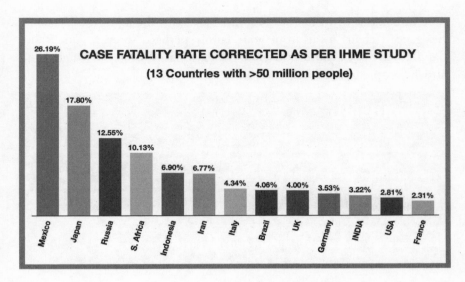

So India has done very well. But propaganda articles (especially in foreign media) and tweets have suggested death tolls of 5x and even 14x the official figures.

The 5x multiple puts India's CFR at 5.45% which is still not too bad if you look at Mexico, Japan, Russia, South Africa, etc. We don't believe even for a second that more than one out of four Covid-positive patients are dying in Mexico, or more than one in six in Japan. Therefore, **if deaths have been underreported by almost all countries, so have the number of cases.**

As far as 14x is concerned, on May 26, 2021, Rahul Gandhi tweeted a *New York Times* article that suggested that India had up to 4.2 million (42 lakh) deaths as of May 24, compared to the official death count of 3,07,231. The American newspaper (more on it in the chapter on journalism) publishing anti-India articles is nothing new. It has been going on since Narendra Modi became the prime ministerial candidate of the BJP/NDA. But was Rahul suggesting that as many as 39 lakh bodies were secretly cremated or buried?

C'mon, Mr Gandhi, be realistic! Criticize Modi and his government for all its mistakes, but stop playing games with death, as what goes around, comes around. **It's called "Karma".** But then, how will you understand Karma, as it's a 'Hindu concept', a religion that you seem to be so unfamiliar with? In your absolute hatred for the man who has taken the 'gaddi' (chair) away from your family perhaps forever, you, Rahul Gandhi, have done more damage to the nation than even the Mughal and British conquerors did.

Conclusion

Yes, India's second wave of Covid-19 has been very severe when you look at the numbers on a standalone basis, but it is not as severe as several other countries have already experienced.

India's cumulative cases per million (from Feb 2020 to 6 May 2021) are only 15.4% of the USA, 17.6% of France, 20.3% of Spain, 22% of Brazil, and much lower than 10 other relatively large countries. India's rank is 110 out of 220 countries, with cases being 80% of the world average as on 12 May 2021.

In cumulative deaths per million, India's tally is 8.6% of Brazil, 9% of the UK, 9.4% of the USA, and sso on. India's rank is 111 and the deaths are 42.8% of the world average as on 12 May.

MOST COUNTRIES IN THE WORLD (including the USA) ARE UNDER-REPORTING DATA.

Comparison of States

Here are the numbers for the cumulative cases per lakh people and tests per 10,000 people for the 19 largest states in India as on May 8, 2021. The reason for using 10,000 instead of one lakh for the testing numbers is so that the chart fits in one page (Delhi's testing numbers would have been 93,277 if we had made it per lakh and would not fit).

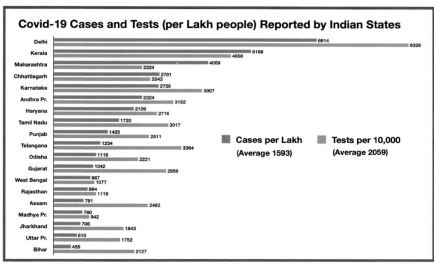

Covid-19 Cases and Tests (per Lakh people) Reported by Indian States

NOTE that the test numbers are for the previous day, as reports come after 24 hours, therefore the same day's testing is not applicable.

The high case numbers in Delhi, Kerala, Maharashtra, and Karnataka are logical, because all four states have a very high percentage of urban population. But, going by the same logic, shouldn't Punjab and Gujarat have reported much higher numbers? And why does Chhattisgarh have such high numbers? Is it lack of health infrastructure or sheer mismanagement?

Were there elections in Delhi, Maharashtra, Chhattisgarh, Karnataka (it had bypolls for only three seats), **Andhra Pradesh, and Haryana? Was Modi campaigning in these six states?**

There have been a lot of reports of Telangana and West Bengal underreporting data. What about Bihar, UP, Jharkhand, MP, Assam, Rajasthan, Gujarat, Odisha, and Punjab?

The testing data gives a better understanding of whether they are testing very little, or underreporting data. It is obvious from the above chart that MP, West Bengal, and Rajasthan have tested the least, followed by UP and Jharkhand. Delhi has the best testing record, at ~4.5x the national average. Kerala is at more than double the national average, followed by Karnataka, Telangana, Andhra Pradesh, Tamil Nadu, and Gujarat. UP's total 4.25 crore tests are 1.47x the next highest state, Maharashtra, which has done 2.89 crore tests, but UP's testing rate per 10 lakhs (one million) is 85.1% of the national average. It was 81.22% just eight days earlier, so the climb is commendable.

But the tests done in Delhi fell 36.1% between May 13–19 compared with April 11–17. Why was this? During the same period, testing went up 76% in Tamil Nadu, 60.5% in West Bengal, 49.3% in MP, 27.6% in UP, and 24% in Bihar. **Should testing be going up or down when the pandemic is at its peak, Mr Kejriwal?**

Here is the chart for the cumulative TPR as on May 8.

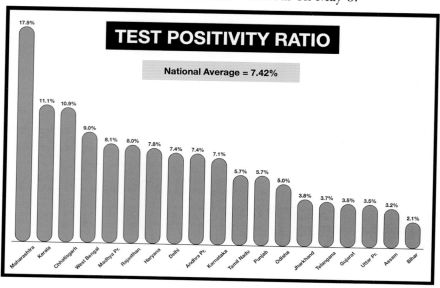

Haryana, Delhi, Andhra Pradesh, and Karnataka are more or less at par with the national average. Why is Maharashtra a humongous 2.36 times the average, and why are Kerala and Chhattisgarh ~50% higher? On the other hand, how are Bihar, Assam, UP, Gujarat, Telangana, Jharkhand, and Odisha so much lower than the average?

There is no explanation for the high TPRs of Maharashtra, Kerala, and Chhattisgarh, but the top four states in this chart are all opposition-rules states. We don't know if this is just a coincidence.

For states with the low figures, we do have a hypothesis. Bihar, Assam, UP, Jharkhand, and Odisha are amongst the most 'poor' states in India. It is therefore likely that the medical infrastructure is less developed and the tests are not done properly. But this argument is not applicable to Gujarat and Telangana, which are amongst the nine richest states. The only explanation for Telangana is that they are underreporting figures, like we have said before. As far as Gujarat is concerned, and epidemiologists can either confirm or trash our theory, it is a predominantly vegetarian state and this may have something to do with it.

There is a more important issue that emerges. If some states have tested wrongly, while some have underreported data, India's cumulative COVID-19 cases have probably been higher by at least 15%.

Now, let us come to the most unpleasant statistic of all—the number of deaths by state (per lakh) as on May 8, 2021.

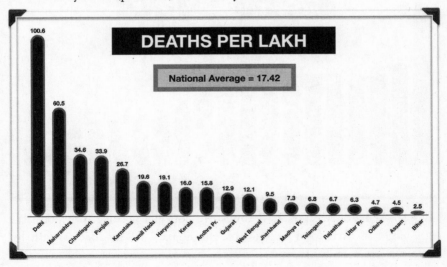

No wonder that India has such a low Death Rate compared with other large countries. Almost no one seems to be dying of COVID-19 in the state ruled by Sushashan Babu (Nitish Kumar). The figures for all states—except Delhi, Maharashtra, Chhattisgarh, Punjab, Karnataka, Tamil Nadu, and Haryana—are unbelievably low, and are definitely underreported. Shame on the governments of all those states. They are almost evenly divided as NDA–ruled or opposition–ruled states, so no single party can be blamed for hiding numbers, but Modi should definitely take the NDA chief ministers to task for their callousness.

Why do Delhi and Maharashtra have such high death numbers? More than 1/775 people in Delhi and 1/1285 in Maharashtra has already lost their lives to COVID-19 as on June 2, 2021!

A shocking piece of data is that Mumbai reported 12.1% "deaths due to other reasons" as compared to COVID-19 related deaths from March 29, 2020 to April 30, 2021 (13 months), but the same figure for February 1, 2021 to April 30, 2021, was 38.5%. In the case of the rest of Maharashtra, the 13–month figure was 0.81%, and the recent three month figure was 0.75%. Is Brihanmumbai Municipal Corporation (BMC) underreporting Mumbai's death figures since the second wave began? These numbers say they are!

Let us also look at the Case Fatality Rate in different states.

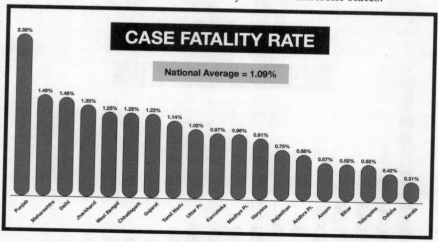

Punjabis are dying at 2.18 times the national average. One possible explanation is their food habits. Epidemiologists will be able to confirm. Malayalis seem to be immortal. *Due to Communist rule?*

Most states with a CFR of 25% or more below the national average are likely to be fudging death figures. These include Rajasthan, Andhra, Assam, Bihar, Telangana, Odisha, and Kerala. OMG, did we just name seven states of which only one has a BJP CM?

We apologize if we have hurt anyone's sentiments, but that is definitely not our intention. Like we said in the 'Notes from the Authors' at the beginning, we too have lost family members to COVID-19. These are data analytics and numbers don't lie.

Gujarat CM Vijay Rupani told *Times Now* that all states are only recording those deaths which have not resulted directly from COVID-19, as a COVID-related death. So, if a patient has a heart attack after developing COVID-19, the reason for death is recorded as a heart attack, and not COVID-19. **This is unacceptable, and all states that have done this need to revise the figures from March 2020 to date. Only then will we know the actual picture. And it could be very scary.**

Let us also look at how bad the COVID-related deaths are, when compared to other leading causes of deaths in India.

COVID-19 DEATH SIMULATOR
A calendar based simulation of Covid-19 deaths compared to historical average of selected India causes.

16 Sep 2020

Coronary Heart Disease	1,145,888	Kidney Disease	189,846	Lung Cancers	63,602
Lung Disease	583,802	Liver Disease	188,191	Breast Cancer	57,501
Stroke	503,044	Suicide	153,772	Cervical Cancer	51,758
Influenza and Pneumonia	439,172	Alzheimers & Dementia	100,333	Drownings	45,566
Tuberculosis	300,201	Birth Trauma	90,018	Stomach Cancer	44,610
Diarrhoeal diseases	291,807	COVID-19	83,230	HIV/AIDS	44,238
Diabetes Mellitus	220,098	Hypertension	81,691	Colon-Rectum Cancers	40,009
Low Birth Weight	215,320	Oral Cancer	72,021	Peptic Ulcer Disease	39,576
Road Traffic Accidents	213,051	Rheumatic Heart Disease	69,209		

8 May 2021

Coronary Heart Disease	2,177,187	Kidney Disease	360,708	Lung Cancers	120,844
Lung Disease	1,109,225	Liver Disease	357,584	Breast Cancer	109,253
Stroke	955,785	Suicide	292,166	Cervical Cancer	98,341
Influenza and Pneumonia	834,427	COVID-19	242,398	Drownings	86,576
Tuberculosis	570,383	Alzheimers & Dementia	190,632	Stomach Cancer	84,759
Diarrhoeal diseases	554,433	Birth Trauma	171,035	HIV/AIDS	84,053
Diabetes Mellitus	418,187	Hypertension	155,213	Colon-Rectum Cancers	76,018
Low Birth Weight	409,109	Oral Cancer	136,841	Peptic Ulcer Disease	75,195
Road Traffic Accidents	404,797	Rheumatic Heart Disease	131,498		

This Table shows us that COVID-19 has become the 13th biggest cause for deaths in India during the second wave, compared with the 15th biggest during the first wave. However, it is causing only 10.5% of the deaths from heart disease, ~21.8% of lung disease, ~25.4% of stroke, ~29% of flu & pneumonia, ~34.6% of all types of cancers, ~42.5% of TB, ~43.7% of diarrhoea-related deaths, ~58% of diabetes-related deaths, and ~59.9% of deaths caused by road accidents.

Before ending this chapter, let us also look at the total vaccine jabs given by states as on May 28. The figures are given separately for the period since May 1 because state governments were given the responsibility to procure vaccines for the 18-45 population, who became eligible for vaccination from that date.

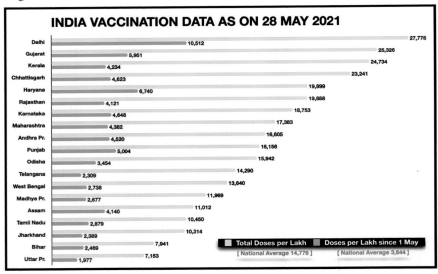

An analysis of the total numbers show that all states with high urbanization—except Tamil Nadu—have done well. Why this is important is because it is much more difficult to reach people in rural areas. After May 1, Delhi, Haryana, Gujarat, and Punjab have done much better than other states in absolute numbers; while Delhi, Assam, Haryana, Bihar, and Punjab have had the best performance when you compare the percentage of jabs given since May 1 to the overall jabs given.

As of June 6, about 19.9% of India's 18+ population had received the first jab, whereas 4.96% had been fully vaccinated.

More than 42.5% of the 60+ population had got their first jabs, while almost 13.5% were fully vaccinated. In the 45-59 age group, more than 39.7% had got their first jabs and over 9% were fully vaccinated.

Contrary to falsehoods being spread by Rahul Gandhi and the Congress party, by June 6, 2021, India had given at least one dose of a COVID-19 vaccine to more than 13.4% of its entire population, compared to the world average of 11.55%.

Where's My Vaccine?

Three COVID-19 vaccines are currently made in India: **Covishield** made by **SII** based on a patent owned and licensed by UK-based AstraZeneca (AZ); the home-developed and produced **Covaxin** by **BB**, and **Sputnik-V** developed by Russia's Gamaleya Institute, and licensed by the Russian Direct Investment Fund (RDIF) to seven Indian companies, of which Panacea Biotech and Hetero Biopharma had started making it by June 1, 2021, but due to the testing and approval process, it will become available only from July/August. Dr Reddy's Labs started importing Sputnik V in May and jabs are already being given to people.

With Modi's push to increase the production of vaccines, between June and October, Covaxin will start getting made by three public sector units (Haffkine in Mumbai, Indian Immunologicals in Hyderabad and BIBCOL in UP), and the capacity will go up from one crore doses/month in February 2021 to 7.5 crore doses/month by August 2021.

Soon, six more COVID-19 vaccines will be made in India.

India's first DNA vaccine for COVID-19 (ZyCov-D) will be made by **Zydus Cadila** and is expected to hit the market by September. Second will be a vaccine developed by **Biological E**, based on US technology. India's first mRNA vaccine (Pfizer and Moderna make mRNA vaccines) for COVID-19 will come from **Gennova** by September. In November, BB and SII will add two more vaccines, a **nasal vaccine by BB**, and **Covovax** to be produced by SII in India under license from Novavax, USA. Biological E will also produce mRNA vaccines licensed from Canadian company Providence from 2022, but they will import up to three crore doses from Canada this year. These dates are based on media reports as on June 3, 2021.

The overall capacity of made-in-India COVID-19 vaccines will go from six crore doses/month in February 2021 to ~33.6 crore doses/month by September 2021 and ~50.3 crores doses/month by November 2021.

The AMB has levelled allegations on Modi that he exported (or allowed the exports of) vaccines instead of using them to vaccinate Indians at home.

Yes, it is correct that India exported 6.637 crore (66.37 million) doses of Covid vaccines to 93 countries between January 20 and April 16, 2021. Out of these, 3.547 crore doses of Covishield and 3.25 lakh doses of Covaxin were sold commercially, while 1.072 crore doses of Covishield and 1.986 crore doses of Covaxin were given free of cost as grants.

India's neighbours got 31.9%, low-income African nations and UN health workers/peacekeepers got 44.3%, and Middle-eastern countries which supply us oil and/or have a huge Indian diaspora, got 8%. **Overall, ~84% of the total exports of vaccines were as per the commercial and licensing compulsions of SII & BB. Besides, what right would India have in asking other countries to continue sending us raw materials for vaccines, if we would not export the end product to other countries?**

> 66
>
> *89.5% of these vaccines left India by the 14th of March, when India had a 7-day moving average of 21,146 cases, or just 21.6% of the first wave's peak.*
>
> *When cases started crossing 25,000 per day almost every day, Prime Minister Modi took a decision on 24th March 2021 to STOP Covid vaccine exports completely.*

The All India Peoples Science Network, a national federation of science networks, issued a statement, urging the Central Government to continue exporting COVID-19 vaccines. No PM or government of a large, diverse and complex country like India can satisfy everyone.

Leading American scientist Dr Peter Hotez, Dean of the National School of Tropical Medicine at Baylor College of Medicine (USA) said that the Pfizer and Moderna vaccines may not impact the world's low and middle income countries, but India's vaccines have "rescued the world" and India's contributions must not be underestimated. It is "India's gift" to the world, Dr Hotez said.

Canadian businessman and investor Patrick Brauckmann said on April 23, *"Important for Canadians and the world not to forget that almost half the vaccines Canada has administered were given to Canada by India because Canada couldn't source enough."* Hundreds (maybe thousands) of people from many other countries have shared similar sentiments.

Australian Cricketer Matthew Hayden said, *"The world media has been quick to judge India … it has spared no time in lambasting a country of 1.4 billion [140 crore] where the sheer numbers make the implementation of any public scheme a challenge. My heart bleeds to see it not only in agony at the moment, but also for the bad press that has been hurled at it by those who I am not sure spend any time here to understand India. **I have always had the highest respect for the leaders who are entrusted with the task of running such a vast country** … India has already vaccinated five times the entire population of Australia."* We don't know when he said this, but by June 6, India had already vaccinated more than nine times the population of Australia.

On January 28, when Modi told the World Economic Forum's (WEF) virtual Davos Summit that India would assist other countries with vaccines, the 7-day moving average of new daily cases was only 13,505 (~0.98 per lakh Indians), and had fallen from 16,347 two weeks earlier. Look at this Table to see how the numbers shot up drastically.

DATE (2021)	Days Since 28 Jan 2021	DAILY CASES (7-day average)	CASES PER LAKH	No. of Times increase from 28 Jan	NEED TO PANIC?
28 Jan	0	13,505	0.98	NA	NO
28 Feb	31	15,240	1.098	1.12	NO
14 March	45	22,269	1.603	1.64	SLIGHT
28 March	59	56,213	4.044	4.13	YES
28 April	90	3,49,038	25.09	25.60	EXTREME
8 May	100	3,92,331	28.194	28.77	EXTREME

Is Modi some kind of superhuman to guess that this would happen, and so soon? A 4.13 times increase in 59 days and a 25.6 times increase in 90 days???

We have factored in the populations on the exact days, and not taken today's population. As the situation was fine even on February 28, why should India have stopped exports? By March 14, 89.5% had already left the country; and the decision to stop exports completely—including unfulfilled commitments of SII towards AZ—was taken within 10 days.

We can blame the elections and the Kumbh Mela, but did these events cause 83.4 lakh infections (83.5% of India's total) between February 26 and May 5 outside Assam, Kerala, Puducherry, Tamil Nadu, Uttarakhand, and West Bengal, at average 1,22,647 cases/day? Or did these events cause 97.25 lakh infections @ 3,24,160 cases/day outside West Bengal, from April 13 (a week after all except the Bengal elections were over) to May 13? Let us be realistic. We shall give some comparison graphs for the 20 largest Indian states in a later chapter.

The Joe Biden government in the US initially refused to send India their unused AZ vaccines (same as Covishield made in India), or raw materials required for Indian companies to make vaccines. *"The United States first and foremost is engaged in an ambitious and effective and, so far, successful effort to vaccinate the American people. It is not only in our interest to see Americans get vaccinated, but it is in the interest of the rest of the world to see Americans vaccinated,"* said a spokesman of the U.S. State Department (their foreign ministry), when asked about raw materials exports to India. Americans think they still own the world, even after China has surpassed them in almost every sphere.

There have been a lot of reports about Microsoft founder and philanthropist **Bill Gates**—the world's fourth richest person—having a hand in this American vaccine terrorism. Gates is alleged to own substantial ownership interests in one or more American vaccine manufacturers.

After Foreign Minister Dr S Jaishankar failed to convince his counterpart Secretary of State Antony Blinken, National Security Advisor Ajit Doval (widely considered the third most powerful man in Modi's government) spoke to his American counterpart Jake Sullivan, and the US cowed down.

What was discussed will remain an 'official secret', but we would not be surprised if it did not have to do with India threatening to blacklist US defence manufacturers from the Modi government's ₹15.5 lakh crore ($210 billion) weapons procurement program, which includes an order of 150 multirole combat jets (114 for the IAF and 36 for the Navy) as soon as the economy revives post-Covid, for an estimated price of ₹1.67 lakh crore ($22.5 billion), for which two American companies—Boeing and Lockheed Martin—are trying very hard, especially after losing the 36 aircraft deal to the French-made Rafale. The American 'Military Industrial Complex' (MIC) is the most powerful body in that country, as Amit has elaborated in his sensational book *USAma—Is USA the World's Largest Terrorist?*

It is much more powerful than the 'pharma lobby' that would have been behind Biden's vaccine terrorism. No politician in the US dare go against the wishes of the MIC. If it was not this reason, why would our NSA have to speak to their NSA? In ideal circumstances, our defence minister should have spoken to his counterpart, but using a translator could have been catastrophic, and we doubt that General Lloyd Austin could have understood the accent of Rajnath Singh, or vice-versa.

Once they had cowed down, not only did the US agree to send us two crore doses of the AZ vaccine (about 1% of India's total requirement), but also agreed to send raw materials for our vaccine manufacturers, and a host of other drugs and medical supplies.

The official statement from the White House (office and residence of the US president) on April 25, 2021, said: "*National Security Advisor Jake Sullivan spoke with National Security Advisor Ajit Doval, expressing deep sympathy for the people of India following the recent spike in COVID-19 cases ... Building on the seven-decade health partnership between the United States (US) and India ... they resolved that India and the US will continue to fight the global pandemic together. Just as India sent assistance to the US as our hospitals were strained early in the pandemic, the US is determined to help India in its time of need. To this end, the US is working around the clock to deploy available resources and supplies. The US has identified sources of specific raw material urgently required for Indian manufacture of the Covishield vaccine that will immediately be made available for India. To help treat COVID-19 patients and protect frontline health workers in India, the US has identified supplies of therapeutics, rapid diagnostic test kits, ventilators, and Personal Protective Equipment (PPE) that will immediately be made available for India. The US also is pursuing options to provide oxygen generation and related supplies on an urgent basis. The U.S. Development Finance Corporation is funding a substantial expansion of manufacturing capability for BiologicalE, the vaccine manufacturer in India, enabling BioE to ramp up to produce at least 1 billion [100 crore] doses of COVID-19 vaccines by the end of 2022."*

Compared to the 6.637 crore doses that were exported, India had given ~23.28 crore doses to people in India in 142 days as on June 6, 2021. Over 18.63 crore Indians had received the first jab, ~20.2% of the number worldwide, which was 14% more than India's 17.7% share of world population.

From April 3 to 31, India managed ~27.88 lakh jabs/day. This fell during May to ~17.97 lakh jabs/day as the all mighty US refused to supply raw materials to SII. This is important because SII made over 89% of all Indian-made vaccines till the end of April. However, once the problem was sorted out with the US, India was once again able to average ~26.85 lakh jabs/day from May 27 to June 8.

On April 24, the GOI removed import duties on vaccines. Many states floated global tenders for importoing vaccines. However, except Russia's RDIF, foreign manufacturers refused to deal with state governments. There were reports that some were asking for kickbacks (not surprising!).

The fall in the rate of vaccination was also because states were to procure vaccines for the population aged 18–45, and many states messed up, as you have seen at the end of the previous chapter. Due to this, as well as a Supreme Court observation, Modi announced on June 7 that the GOI was taking charge of vaccine procurement.

See this graph of the number of people who have received at least one dose (as of June 5) in seven large countries which had given the most jabs, excluding China whose numbers no one believes. India is right on top, and had given 6.3% more jabs than even the US despite starting vaccination 33 days after them.

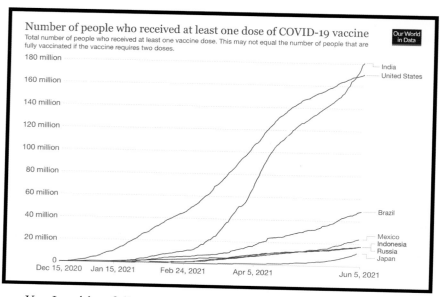

Yes, Israel has fully vaccinated 59.32% of its population as of June 2 and this fact has been much talked about in the media and on WhatsApp chats, saying India should follow Israel's example. In the same way, comparisons with small countries such as Chile, Bahrain, Serbia, Aruba,

Do the intellectuals who say such nonsense even understand basic math? Israel's population is just 0.66% India's.

As of June 2, India has given 20.12 times the number of vaccine doses that Israel has done.

Hungary, Qatar, and Uruguay—which the *Times of India* made on May 5, 2021—do not make sense.

By May 28, the 27 European Union (EU) nations with 5.62 times India's total GDP and average 17.9 times India's per-capita GDP were able to manage only 1.12 times the vaccination numbers that India had achieved.

Amit's German friend told him that she has not even got a single dose, as only those aged 60+ and special categories such as healthcare workers were eligible. Another friend in Canada said that his wife and he waited for their first jab for over three months, and now have to wait for another four months for their second jab, as India has stopped vaccine exports to Canada.

Let us move on to global vaccine production numbers. Contrary to popular belief, **India is NOT the world's largest COVID-19 vaccine manufacturer**. India is the world's largest producer of all types of vaccines, not specifically for COVID vaccines, in which category it is the fourth largest. Look at this chart of the world's largest vaccine manufacturers and the number of doses they are expected to produce in one year from May 2021 to April 2022. (Disclaimer: *This is not an exhaustive list*).

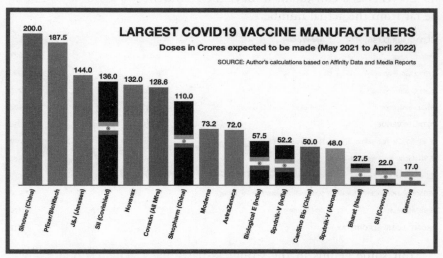

Typically, vaccines take years to be developed and go through three phases of clinical trials before being approved for public use in developed countries. But the first COVID-19 vaccine was developed and released in less than a year since the outbreak was declared a pandemic. The WHO issued an emergency-use listing (ELU) for the Pfizer–BioNTech vaccine on December 31, 2020, and granted ELUs to two versions of the Oxford–AstraZeneca vaccine manufactured by SII in India and SKBio in South Korea on February 15, 2021. Currently, 82 vaccine candidates are under clinical development and 180+ are in the pre-clinical development phase. This all adds up to a remarkable achievement in global public healthcare.

There were controversies raised by the Congress, AAP, TMC, and other members of the AMB, about prices of Covishield and Covaxin being higher for states than for the Centre. SII is selling Covishield to the Centre at ₹150, states at ₹300, and to private hospitals at ₹600. The price for the Centre had been decided back in October 2020, and SII makes a loss on each dose at that price.

Here are Amit's assumptions for SII's and BB's financials, up to the time that India's entire vaccine needs are met (November 2021).

Yes, SII is projected to make a loss till end-November 2021,when India's vaccine needs will be fully met, as we will demonstrate later. Of course, SII will make substantial profits from exports after that.

Amit has worked on more than enough financial studies/models in his 20 years as a consultant to have the confidence to say that he cannot be far from the actual numbers.

COVISHIELD (SII)	Assumptions	Doses in Crore	Price in ₹	Amount in ₹ Crores
Export		4.619	265	1,224
Central Government		26.600	150	3,990
State Governments		37.400	300	11,220
Private Hospitals	20% of all domestic doses	16.000	600	9,600
TOTAL REVENUE		84.619		26,034
LESS: 50% to AstraZeneca	Royalty as per Contract			-13,017
LESS: Manufacturing Cost		84.619	100	-8,462
LESS: Administration Cost	₹10 crore per month for 17 months			-170
LESS: Recovery of Investment	$800 million investment (*Forbes*)			-5,900
LESS: Interest	@14% Interest			-1,170
PROFIT (LOSS) BEFORE TAX				-1,515

But some genius in the Congress party has calculated that SII will make a profit of ₹35,350 crores, by assuming that private hospitals will buy 50% of the doses. We believe the assumption of 20% is far more realistic. As per the Congress, SII's profits from Covishield will be ₹350 per dose. To achieve this, SII will have to sell Covishield at an average price of ₹900 per dose (₹450 pay-out to AZ; ₹100 manufacturing cost) and not recover any investments or costs. As the highest price slab is ₹600 for private hospitals, how will they get an average of ₹900? Can the genius in Congress explain? If Rahul Gandhi did the calculations himself, then we understand, don't we?

Here are Amit's calculations for Bharat Biotech. Yes, BB will make big profits as it doesn't have to pay royalties to a foreign licensor, unlike SII. We have assumed that private hospitals will only consume 5% of their production as their price of ₹1200 is too high.

COVAXIN (BB)	Assumptions	Doses in Crore	Price in ₹	Amount in ₹ Crores
Export		2.019	207	417
Central Government		10.000	166	1,664
State Governments		23.060	400	9,224
Private Hospitals	5% of all domestic doses	1.740	1,200	2,088
License Fee Earned from Other Manufacturers		17.500	40	700
TOTAL REVENUE		**36.819**		**14,093**
LESS: Recovery of Investment				-2,750
LESS: Manufacturing Cost		36.819	100	-3,682
LESS: Administration Cost	₹7 crore per month for 17 months			-119
LESS: Recovery of Interest	@14% Interest			-545
PROFIT BEFORE TAX				**6,997**

But the Congress genius has assumed their profits at ₹75,750 crores, with a whole lot of wrong assumptions, especially that private hospitals will buy 50.5 crore doses at ₹1200.

All the calculations of the Congress party are based on only the 18-44 population, as the GOI is taking care of the 45+ population. As per the Congress, 25.25 crore Indians aged 18-44 will pay ₹1600–2500 for two doses for Covishield and another 25.25 crore people will pay ₹2900–3400 for two doses of Covaxin. So, as per them, 83.9% of Indians aged 18-44 will pay ₹4800–11,700 for vaccines for a family of three. Really, Mr Gandhi, do you think 83.9% of Indians are as wealthy as you?

Please note that after this chapter was completed and on the day prior to the book going for printing (June 7), Prime Minister Modi announced that the GOI will provide vaccines free of cost at government hospitals for the entire population aged 18+, that private hospitals could procure up to 25% of the production of Indian vaccine manufacturers, and that the private hospitals could charge maximum ₹150 per jab as service charge over and above the cost of the vaccine.

Consider that the price of Russian and Chinese vaccines is more than ₹900, and that of American vaccines is more than ₹1100–1500, SII's price of ₹300 and ₹600 is not bad at all, and BB's price of ₹400 is also fine. But BB definitely needs to reduce the ₹1200 price being charged to private hospitals. Does Dr Ella want to become Mukesh Ambani overnight?

The Congress and other opposition parties, as well as author Chetan Bhagat raised a hue and cry to allow import of Pfizer vaccines. All the noise was only for Pfizer, there were no asks for Janssen,

Novavax, or Moderna. Why? Is there any financial interest involved? We wouldn't be surprised if there is.

In early December 2020, Pfizer was the first foreign company to seek emergency–use approval in India but it did not attend subsequent meetings called by our Central Drugs Standard Control Organisation. Pfizer sought to import and distribute its vaccine without doing local trials in India. "*Based on … our understanding of additional information that the regulator may need, the company has decided to withdraw its application at this time*," Pfizer said in a statement to *Reuters* on February 5, 2021, adding that it will in the future look to resubmit its application with the additional information that the Indian regulator requires. Pfizer had also wanted the Indian government to sign indemnity bonds that protect the company from being sued in case their vaccine ends up causing any side-effects. There are also unconfirmed reports that the GOI wanted the vaccines at less than ₹600 per dose, but Pfizer wanted more than three times that price.

There are many other important things to understand about Pfizer's vaccine. The US Government had to return several thousand doses after they became 'too cold' during the transportation process. Also, as dry ice transport by air poses a cabin pressure risk, it is restricted by the US Federal Aviation Administration to 15,000 lbs (~6,804 kgs), or maximum 10 lakh doses per flight. This was increased from a pre–COVID limit of 3,000 lbs. Not all states or cities follow the federal guidelines, and most air transport within the US is still only 3-4 lakh doses per flight. This is also the average quantity Japan and Israel get per flight.

Considering that India needed total ~188.8 crore doses for the population aged 2+ (the calculations are given later), even if the Pfizer vaccine met only 30% of our needs (~56.64 crore doses), it would mean 1,618 flights @ 3-4 lakh doses per flight. This would cost ₹6828 crores @ ₹4.22 crores for a chartered 38–hour round–trip flight including loading and unloading time between the US and India (as the aircrafts would have to return empty). Add another ₹186 crores @ ₹11.50 lakhs for a 4–hour round–trip chartered domestic flight (average to cover all airports across India from Delhi, Mumbai, Bengaluru, and Kolkata). Was Rahul Gandhi planning to donate ₹7014 crores for this noble cause from the very rich Rajiv Gandhi Foundation, which has received donations/grants from the inventors of the Wuhan virus (Coronavirus), or was Chetan Bhagat going to donate it?

Next, consider the fact that Pfizer vaccines need ultra-low temperature (ULT) of -60ºC to -80ºC, much colder than a normal freezer (-20ºC) or fridge. **Covishield and Covaxin need 2º to 8ºC, and an ordinary fridge is sufficient**. Pfizer requires specialised ULT containers (₹14-18 lakhs each) and trucks for transport from the airports to hospitals in 8,000+ Indian towns. Each hospital will need ULT freezers (₹3-20 lakhs each), depending on the number of vaccines they need to store. Add everything, and the cost of vaccinating 30% of India with the Pfizer vaccine would be staggering.

All these hurdles make it very difficult and costly to scale up distribution of the Pfizer vaccine. That's why Pfizer has been focused on North America. More than ₹175 per dose is just the cost of storage and transport for the Pfizer vaccine.

Most importantly, given its production volumes and existing supply commitments, Pfizer can supply maximum ~35 lakh doses per week to India. Assuming this triples to 105 lakh doses per week in 26 weeks, meeting 30% of India's demand will take Pfizer ~71.3 weeks or ~16½ months. Amit had written this in an article published in GoaChronicle on May 15, 2021 and the same was confirmed as per several news reports 9-10 days later.

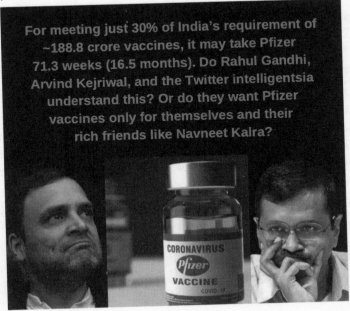

For meeting just 30% of India's requirement of ~188.8 crore vaccines, it may take Pfizer 71.3 weeks (16.5 months). Do Rahul Gandhi, Arvind Kejriwal, and the Twitter intelligentsia understand this? Or do they want Pfizer vaccines only for themselves and their rich friends like Navneet Kalra?

Even if Pfizer sold its vaccine to India at a generous price of $25 (₹1850) per dose, we are talking about a cost of ₹2025 per dose for the hospital, including the additional logistics costs that we have talked about. Pfizer vaccines cost $47 (₹3480) per dose in Israel. The price of $19.50 (₹1443) per dose in the US was only for the first 100 million doses. The company renegotiates prices for every order and has stalled deliveries until new orders are paid.

See in this Statista graphic how Pfizer and AstraZeneca's profits have gone up by 45% and 167% in January-March 2021 compared with January-March 2020. If Pfizer somehow managed to sell 56.64 crore doses to India in a record time of six months at a 'low' price of $25,

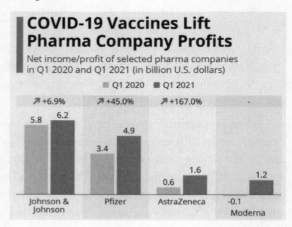

COVID-19 Vaccines Lift Pharma Company Profits

Net income/profit of selected pharma companies in Q1 2020 and Q1 2021 (in billion U.S. dollars)

■ Q1 2020   ■ Q1 2021

	Johnson & Johnson	Pfizer	AstraZeneca	Moderna
+6.9%	5.8 / 6.2			
+45.0%		3.4 / 4.9		
+167.0%			0.6 / 1.6	
-				-0.1 / 1.2

it gets revenues of $14.16 billion. Imagine the profits. Assuming Pfizer made a profit margin of only 15% at the $19.50 price it sold the first 100 million doses to the US government, it will make a 33.7% profit at $25. That translates to a profit of $4.77 billion (₹35,300 crores) in six months (two quarters) by selling to India, an increase of almost 50% from its Q1 2021 (January-March 2021) profit shown in this graphic.

Is that why the Biden government refused to give us their unused AZ vaccines, as well as raw materials required by Indian vaccine makers? To help Pfizer specifically? Or to help all those American pharma and biotech companies that are involved in COVID-19 vaccine terrorism?

Arvind Kejriwal wrote to Prime Minister Modi that the formulae of Covaxin and Covishield should be shared with other capable pharma companies. We are shocked that the IIT-graduate Mr. Kejriwal does not understand that the formula of Covishield is owned by AZ, not by SII or Modi. Besides, the formula of Covaxin is already being shared with the three PSUs that we have named in the second paragraph, and BB has already agreed to share it with any company that can produce the vaccine.

Anyway, the most important thing is to understand by what date the entire Indian population above the age of two (2) years will get fully vaccinated. This Table first explains India's requirements, and it is very important for all educated Indians to understand it properly.

Sub-Set of Population	Total People in Crores	% who will refuse vaccine	% out of reach	Total % Unvaccinated	People to be vaccinated	Vaccine need in Crores
Urban 18+	33.81	15.00%	0%	15.00%	28.739	57.478
Rural 18+	59.90	30.00%	5%	35.00%	38.935	77.870
TOTAL 18+	93.71	24.59%		27.78%	67.674	135.348
Urban age 6-17	10.75	20.00%	0%	20.00%	8.600	17.200
Rural age 6-17	21.35	40.00%	5%	45.00%	11.743	23.486
TOTAL age 6-17	32.10	33.20%		36.63%	20.343	40.686
Urban age 2-5	1.92	20.00%	0%	20.00%	1.536	3.072
Rural age 2-5	4.04	45.00%	5%	50.00%	2.020	4.040
TOTAL age 2-5	5.96	36.95%		40.34%	3.556	7.112
GRAND TOTAL	131.77	27.27%		30.51%	91.573	183.146

The assumed 27.27% who will refuse to get vaccinated is a conservative estimate, and the real percentage is likely to be higher, thus further reducing the need for vaccines. Don't forget that ~35% of Indians live in backward areas, and are generally against modern science, preferring to rely upon home remedies, tribal medicines, and the likes.

Of the assumed 67.674 crore adult (18+) population who are candidates for vaccination, ~27.6% had already received their first jabs and ~6.84% their second jab by June 6, 2021.

Accounting for ~3% overall wastage, **India has a requirement of ~139.53 crore doses for the 18+ population, ~41.94 crore for ages 6–17, and ~7.33 crore for ages 2–5, or a total of about 188.8 crore doses.** The current national vaccine wastage is ~6.3%. It is the highest in three opposition-ruled states: Jharkhand (37.3%), Chhattisgarh (30.2%), and Tamil Nadu (15.5%).

Almost 23.28 crore doses were already given and over 1.49 crore doses were available with states as of June 6, 2021. This brings down the requirement to ~164 crore additional doses as on June 6. So by what date will everyone get vaccinated?

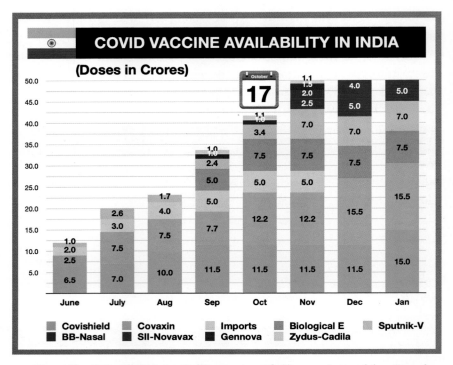

Yes, all adults (18+) in India can get fully vaccinated by October 17, 2021 as per these detailed calculations, subject to there being enough vaccination centres and nurses/technicians who can give the jabs.

But this data disproves the claim of many people in opposition parties, and other members of the AMB, that it will take 44 or 63 months for all 18+ Indians to get two jabs. One lady (we believe she was a Trinamool or Left supporter, not sure which) said on TV that it will take 11 years. Maybe she gets her data from the ISI or the Pakistan Army!

Even if the domestic production and imports don't increase further, all children and adolescents aged 2–17 can also be vaccinated by November 16 this year.

We can thus hope that there will be lesser critical cases and lesser deaths due to COVID-19 in India in the year 2022 and beyond, till the pandemic lasts, if its lasts beyond February-March 2022 at all.

The government has grossly overestimated India's vaccine needs as it has not factored it the 27.27% (or any number for that matter) for the number of people who will refuse to get vaccinated or those for whom the vaccines will be out of reach, and that's the reason it is estimating the vaccination drive to go up to the end of December or even beyond.

The AMB keeps asking why the GOI did not (1) get Indian companies to ramp up production earlier; and (2) why did the GOI not import large quantities of vaccines. While both questions may look very relevant without knowing all the facts, let us do exactly that.

Firstly, SII and BB combined had personally promised to the PM that they will produce 20 crore doses per month, but at 8.5 crore, they have been as much as 57.5% short of this target. India is not the only country that has had to delay vaccination. Did you know that, as per Affinity, **out of 83.7 crore doses of vaccines which were projected to be manufactured worldwide in 2020, only 3.7% were actually produced?** India has actually done much better.

Seeing that SII and BB were not meeting targets, on March 17, 2021, a day after cases started crossing 25,000 for the first time since December 18, 2020, the MoHFW set up an intergovernmental panel to explore how to ramp up vaccine production. Obviously, their decisions would take at least five to six months to fructify as it takes minimum that time to set up a COVID-19 vaccine manufacturing facility, and the results are evident from the above chart.

Secondly, when Modi announced the vaccination program in December 2020, many leading opposition politicians asked their voters and followers not to take the vaccines, as either they were not safe, or their efficacy had not been tested properly.

"I will not get vaccinated. It's the BJP's vaccine. The BJP can't be trusted," said Samajwadi chief and former UP chief minister **Akhilesh Yadav.** This was also a message to the people of the people of UP, which comprises >17.4% of India's population.

Throughout January and February 2021, **several Congress leaders came out strongly against the homemade Covaxin**. Anand Sharma, a former Union Minister, questioned the approval granted to Covaxin. *"The Health Ministry needs to give cogent reasons for dispensing with mandatory protocols and requirements, since it involves the health and safety of those frontline workers who will be vaccinated,"* Shashi Tharoor, Jairam Ramesh, Manish Tewari, and Randeep Surjewala also spoke up against the use of Covaxin. Yet, former PM Dr Manmohan Singh and his wife got two jabs of Covaxin each.

Punjab and Chhattisgarh (ruled by Congress), Jharkhand (Congress alliance government), and Left–ruled Kerala refused to use Covaxin. Surprisingly, Kerala and Chhattisgarh are amongst the four top states in terms of vaccine jabs administered per lakh population.

The anti-Modi brigade is directly responsible for over 75,000 deaths.

Three rumours were being circulated in Aligarh Muslim University: (1) People die soon after getting vaccinated; (2) Vaccines lead to infertility and impotency; and (3) People get infected after getting the vaccine. Such was the impact of these unscientific rumours that the number of vaccination centres at Aligarh had to be reduced due to low turnout and a general lack of enthusiasm among the public to get vaccinated. This resulted in several deaths at AMU, including 38 teachers.

Rahul Gandhi had not taken even the first dose till April 11 and was tested COVID-19 positive on April 20.

Bajaj Auto MD Rajiv Bajaj spoke against vaccination. Supreme Court lawyer Prashant Bhushan was a cofounder of AAP who later left the party. He was amongst a group of lawyers who woke up the Chief Justice of India in July 2015 after midnight to have a court hearing for pardoning Yakub Memon, who was to be hanged to death for his role in financing the 12 serial bombings in Mumbai in one day in 1993, which had resulted in 257 deaths and over 1,400 injuries. He tweeted on February 1: "*[Finance Minister Nirmala Sitharaman] announces 35,000 Crores of our money to be spent on private vaccine companies for untested vaccines at a time when Covid is naturally dying down in India … Wah FM sahiba!*"

The media of course was not far behind. AMB news websites *Scroll* and *Quartz India* wrote in December 2020, "*Distrust in Modi could add to vaccine hesitancy …*" The *Quint* wrote on January 4, 2021, "*Those critiquing the Narendra Modi government on the inadequate information provided on COVID vaccine approval were met with the tag of 'anti-national' on social media.*" '*Majority Indians have natural immunity.*

Vaccinating entire population can cause great harm', screamed a headline in *The Print* on January 11.

Alleged journalist Swati Chaturvedi tweeted from her infamous handle @bainjal in January that she has zero faith in Bharat Biotech and that she will not be getting herself vaccinated with Covaxin. She also wrote: "*Yet, bhakts Narendra Modi and Amit Shah should take the vaccine publicly.*" Well, they did. So did the President and the Vice President of India, and several other Central government ministers, as well as the BJP's chief ministers and state government ministers.

Arundhati Roy, who is more of an activist than an author, and who supports Kashmiri separatists, amongst several other antinational causes (see her Wikipedia page), wrote in *The Guardian* of the UK that the two India-made vaccines are amongst the most expensive vaccines in the world, which was a complete lie. In April 2020, she had claimed that COVID-19 is not even a crisis in India and the Modi government is misusing it only to kill Muslims.

This opposition from the AMB is one of the main reasons we have calculated that 27.27% of Indians will refuse to take vaccines.

Cartoonist Satish Acharya tweeted his own photo taking his first vaccine dose on April 18. Until five days prior, for over three months, he has been making fun of the government's vaccination drive. See these cartoons and judge for yourself. Go to his Twitter timeline and you will see that over 90% of his political cartoons are anti-Modi, his government, the BJP, and Modi's known supporters like Arnab Goswami and Baba Ramdev. **Since Acharya's anti-vaccine cartoons are estimated to have been seen by over 2.4 crore people—he could be responsible for at least 6,000 deaths.**

All this opposition was despite the fact that leading doctors had in early January itself spoken in favour of 'both' Indian-made vaccines. Amongst them, the AIIMS Delhi director Dr Randeep Guleria said that we should trust the expert committees that have recommended the vaccines and move forward, as it is the only way to defeat the pandemic. *"We do not have any antiviral drug against the coronavirus, vaccine is our only hope. We should be proactive in rolling out the vaccine as soon as possible and should not get into controversies."* Dr Naresh Trehan, chairman of the Medanta group of hospitals, said that both the vaccines' efficacy and safety had been established through trials.

With all this opposition, how could the small (compared with the much larger SII) Bharat Biotech have taken the risk of increasing its production capacity for Covaxin? SII increased its capacity and was therefore able to start producing six crore doses per month from April. But BB took the decision to expand its capacity only after the President and Vice President of India, the PM, and several Central ministers took Covaxin jabs in the first week of March. That's the reason BB is two months behind in the scaled–up production.

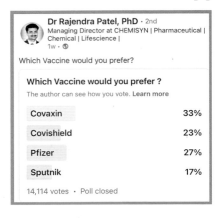

A report on May 21 said that 0.61 cases of blood clots per million jabs of Covishield had been reported, versus zero in the case of Covaxin.

Look at the situation just two and a half months later. In this poll conducted on LinkedIn which was answered by 14,114 people, BB's Covaxin has scored far ahead of any other vaccine amongst the four choices, including SII's Covishield.

Now let us address the question of why the Modi government did not import vaccines. Which ones would they import? We have already given a detailed explanation for Pfizer.

Johnson & Johnson (Janssen) applied for approval only on April 20, 2021, after it was already too late, but their single-dose vaccine is expected to be approved soon. This vaccine, however, has run into trouble with the US calling for a pause in its use after six women developed a rare and severe form of blood clotting after receiving the jab.

India's Council of Scientific & Industrial Research (CSIR) has been in talks with Moderna for around seven months to bring its vaccine to India, but the American company is not interested.

SII is supposed to manufacture Novavax in India under the brand name of Covovax, but the original schedule of starting manufacturing in June has been delayed to October, due to the non-supply of raw materials by the US, which only got sorted in the first week of June.

The Russian Sputnik COVID-19 vaccine got approval in India on April 12 within a month of filing its application to the DGCI.

That leaves Chinese vaccines—do you want Chinese vaccines?

Pfizer-BioNTech 100 million doses
Johnson & Johnson 100 million doses
Moderna 200 million doses
AstraZeneca-Oxford 300 million doses
Novavax 100 million doses
Sanofi-GlaxoSmithKline 100 million doses

The US, under its "Operation Warp Speed" (for Trump-haters and Joe Biden–Kamala Harris fans, fact is that this operation was started by President Donald Trump in May 2020), invested $12.4 billion (₹91,740 crores) in 'potential' COVID-19 vaccines to be made by six companies. The operation aimed to provide at least 300 million (30 crore) doses of vaccines by January 2021, and 900 million in total.

This move by the Trump government amounts to what is commonly referred to as 'vaccine nationalism', whereby countries by pre-ordering vaccines, block the availability to other countries.

Wealthy countries—mainly the US, the 27 EU nations, Japan, Israel, Australia and Canada—signed pre-orders for over 200 crore doses. Germany gave €375 million (₹3340 crores) and €300 million (₹2670 crores), respectively, to German vaccine companies BioNTech (Pfizer's partner) and CureVac.

There have also been concerns regarding price discrimination practices by vaccine manufacturers. South Africa reported that it acquired 15 lakh doses of the AZ vaccine at $5.25 (₹388.50), more than double of the $2.15 price paid by the EU.

Considering that India needed ~188.8 crore vaccines for the entire population aged 2+ which wants to get vaccinated, including wastage and the vaccines already administered, and assuming an average price of ₹1400 as a major proportion of the vaccines would need to be imported, could the GOI have invested ₹2.645 lakh crores for a similar operation, and that too within four months (by March 10, 2021) if the GOI had to save people from the second wave?

TO SAVE PEOPLE FROM THE SECOND WAVE, INDIA WOULD HAVE NEEDED TO GIVE 188.8 CRORE VACCINE JABS BY MARCH 10, 2021, WHEN THE WHOLE WORLD HAD GIVEN ONLY 33.017 CRORE TOTAL JABS. MAYBE THE ANTI–MODI BRIGADE HAD SOME MAGIC.

The amount that the US invested was only 0.055% of their GDP and the amount that India would need to invest would be ~2% of our GDP, or about 36.3 times that of the US.

The US spent $778 billion (₹57.57 lakh crores) on defence in 2020, which was more than the combined expenditure of the next 11 countries combined—China, India, Russia, the UK, Saudi Arabia, Germany, France, Japan, South Korea, Italy, and Australia.

Maybe we should have spent 36.3 times our GDP than the US, but a wiser decision was perhaps taken to be *aatmanirbhar* (self-reliant). After all, no one was expecting such a severe second wave and no expert predicted that the number of COVID-19 infections would rise so soon once the second wave started.

Please read our conclusions below about India's total vaccination demand and supply, about why the vaccination program has been delayed, when we will all get vaccinated, and some global comparisons.

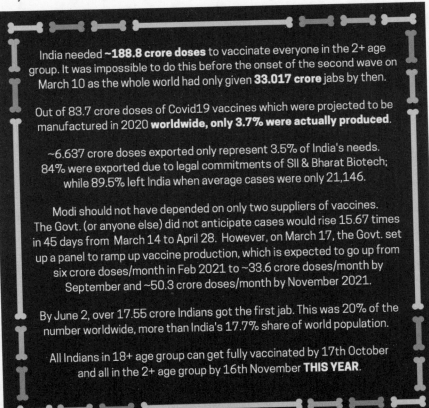

India needed **~188.8 crore doses** to vaccinate everyone in the 2+ age group. It was impossible to do this before the onset of the second wave on March 10 as the whole world had only given **33.017 crore** jabs by then.

Out of 83.7 crore doses of Covid19 vaccines which were projected to be manufactured in 2020 **worldwide, only 3.7% were actually produced**.

~6.637 crore doses exported only represent 3.5% of India's needs. 84% were exported due to legal commitments of SII & Bharat Biotech; while 89.5% left India when average cases were only 21,146.

Modi should not have depended on only two suppliers of vaccines. The Govt. (or anyone else) did not anticipate cases would rise 15.67 times in 45 days from March 14 to April 28. However, on March 17, the Govt. set up a panel to ramp up vaccine production, which is expected to go up from six crore doses/month in Feb 2021 to ~33.6 crore doses/month by September and ~50.3 crore doses/month by November 2021.

By June 2, over 17.55 crore Indians got the first jab. This was 20% of the number worldwide, more than India's 17.7% share of world population.

All Indians in 18+ age group can get fully vaccinated by 17th October and all in the 2+ age group by 16th November **THIS YEAR**.

2-DG a Game–Changer?

A piece of good news is that the DGCI (Drugs Controller General of India) approved a new oral drug that promises to reduce hospitalisation time and oxygen dependency for moderate to severe COVID-19 cases. The 2-DG (2-deoxy-D-glucose) drug developed by INMAS (Institute of Nuclear Medicine and Allied Sciences), a part of DRDO, in partnership with leading pharma company Dr Reddy's Laboratories (DRL) has proved to be effective in clinical trials conducted on 330 patients across 27 hospitals.

The drug started getting used on moderate to severe COVID-19 patients in Hyderabad on May 17, 2021. Mass production started in June. The drug comes in powder form in a sachet and is taken orally by dissolving in water, much like dozens of 'gas' medicines which are very popular in India. **Work on the drug had started back in April 2020**.

DRDO took the initiative of developing the anti–Covid therapeutic application of the 2-DG drug. In April 2020, during the first wave, INMAS–DRDO scientists conducted laboratory experiments with the help of CCMB (Centre for Cellular and Molecular Biology), Hyderabad and found that this molecule works effectively against the SARS-CoV-2 virus (Coronavirus) and inhibits the viral growth. Based on these results, CDSCO (Central Drugs Standard Control Organization) permitted Phase-II clinical trials of 2-DG in COVID-19 patients in May 2020.

The DRDO, along with DRL, started the clinical trials to test the safety and efficacy of the drug in COVID-19 patients. In Phase-II trials conducted on 110 patients from May to October 2020, the drug was found to be safe in COVID-19 patients and showed significant improvement in their recovery. Phase IIa was conducted in six hospitals and Phase IIb (dose ranging) clinical trial was conducted at 11 hospitals all over India.

Patients treated with 2-DG showed faster symptomatic cure than Standard of Care (SoC) on various endpoints. A significantly favourable trend (2½ days' difference) was seen in terms of the median time to achieving normalisation of specific vital signs parameters when compared to SoC.

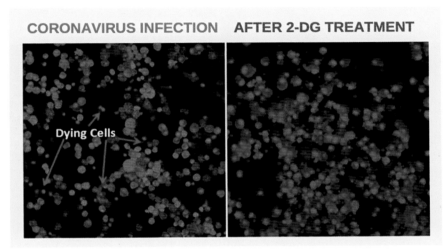

Based on successful results, the DCGI permitted Phase-III clinical trials in November 2020, which were conducted on 220 patients from December 2020 to March 2021 at 27 COVID-19 hospitals in 10 states spread across India. The detailed data of phase-III clinical trial was presented to the DCGI. Significantly higher proportion of patients improved symptomatically and became free from supplemental oxygen dependence (42% vs 31%) by Day–3 in comparison to SoC, indicating an early relief from oxygen therapy/dependence. A similar trend was observed in patients aged over 65 years.

On May 1, the DCGI granted permission for Emergency Use of 2-DG as adjunct therapy in moderate to severe COVID-19 patients. Being a generic molecule and analogue of glucose, it can be easily produced and made available in plenty in the country.

Being a mimic of D-Glucose, the 2-DG drug gets easy passage into the cells where the Coronavirus is already present. Glucose breaks down into two to three carbon compounds, one of them being pyruvate anion, with release of energy. It is a metabolic process called glycolysis. It is this energy on which all living organisms survive. The Coronavirus also survives on this energy. Unlike D-Glucose, 2-DG is unfit for glycolysis. No energy is evolved. Sustaining life becomes difficult and as such, **the Coronavirus dies within a week due to want of energy. This drug also lowers the oxygen dependence and reduces the hospital stay of patients**. It works as an anti-tumour/anti-cancer drug by the same mechanism.

If it is able to destroy the killer Coronavirus, crores of precious lives will be saved, and it's going to be one of the greatest inventions of modern times.

The drug comes in powder form in sachet, which is taken orally by dissolving it in water. It accumulates in the virus–infected cells and prevents virus growth by stopping viral synthesis and energy production. Its selective accumulation in virally infected cells makes this drug unique. In simple terms, the principle is "Cheat the cheater"! Any virus, once inside the body, makes its own copies by cheating our human cells and takes their protein to multiply itself. The brilliant thought process of the scientists at INMAS–DRDO, CCMB, and DRL was simple. For every doubling of the virus cell, it needs energy (glucose). So, the medicine is simply a "Pseudo Glucose" which the multiplying virus intakes but this glucose makes it neutral (unable to multiply). Thus, once the rapid multiplication of the Coronavirus is halted, our own antibodies can readily combat it and overpower it within hours. According to some people, this is simply genius, and we should be proud of Indian scientists!

However, several doctors and scientists have said two very important things: (1) This drug should be only used as a support treatment for COVID-19 and not as a primary treatment; and (2) It should be prescribed by doctors based on the patient's medical condition (oxygen saturation level below 9) and not be allowed to be taken by patients on their own accord. But we all know that maintaining the second guideline will be next to impossible in India, where 'prescription drugs' are easily sold by pharmacies without a prescription.

Not surprisingly, the anti-Modi media has already started their negative publicity against the possibly miraculous 2-DG drug.

Soon after the GOI's announcement about the approval of 2-DG, Ronak Borana wrote in *The Wire*: "*The approval for 2-DG is based on poor* evidence. *2-DG is a modified glucose molecule that has been found to have some therapeutic value as an anticancer and antiviral agent. Research on 2-DG goes as far back as 1956, although it hasn't been approved to treat any other diseases yet. It is currently mostly used in diagnostic testing and research-related activities.* The Wire *couldn't find any preprint or peer-reviewed research paper uploaded by the DRDO and DRL team on 2-DG clinical trials vis-à-vis COVID-19. Instead, we had to rely on publicly available information, like a press release – from the Ministry of Defence."*

Well, *The Wire* may not know that DRDO comes under the Ministry of Defence!!

The anti-Modi news website continued: *"In news reports about the 2-DG approval, the most widely used image is from an in vitro study of 2-DG against SARS-CoV-2. In vitro refers to studies performed outside a biological entity – like the human body or humanised mice. Studies conducted inside a biological entity are called in vivo. As it happens, according to one preprint paper, members of the Patanjali Research Institute and others suggested the use of 2-DG last year. It was based, of all things, on a computer simulation. This image shows that cell cultures in a laboratory without 2-DG had more viral plaques – clear spots indicating cell damage by the virus – compared to the ones with 2-DG. These studies were conducted at CCMB, Hyderabad. While these experiments show that 2-DG can inhibit viral growth, they tell us little about its efficacy in humans.*

"For example, a study published in August 2020 found that around 90 drugs that had been approved by the US Food and Drug Administration had antiviral activity against SARS-CoV-2 – as did ivermectin, hydroxychloroquine, doxycycline, did azithromycin and lopinavir. But none of them has been found to have any meaningful effect in human trials with COVID-19 patients. Based on the results from this in vitro *trial, the national drug regulator had approved a phase 2 trial for 2-DG – possibly in May 2020.* The Wire *couldn't find entries for any of the trials in the Clinical Trial Registry of India (CTRI). The reason for this discrepancy is unclear; emails to the principal investigators of both studies hadn't elicited a response at the time of publishing this article. The only phase 2 trial registered for 2-DG involved 40 patients across 12 sites. If the 2-DG trials haven't been registered, they would be in violation of the ICMR's ethics guidelines.*

"The DRDO and DRL conducted the 2-DG phase 3 trial in 220 patients at 26 sites around the country. However, the CTRI registration of this

trial does not mention which parameters the trial researchers plan to measure. For example, the Phase 2 registration says that the trial's primary endpoint – the main objective of the study – would be to measure the improvement of trial participants on a 10-point scale. The secondary endpoint includes around 15 other measurements, like mortality, improvement in symptoms, time spent with supplemental oxygen, etc. So the trial will be deemed to be successful only if the researchers measure a significant positive change on the primary endpoints – which in 2-DG's case the researchers were marking on the 10-point scale. The CTRI registration of the phase 3 trial, however, doesn't disclose what the primary endpoints were."

But didn't they say that CTRI registration was not done? or maybe we read something wrong in *The Wire* article.

The article continues: *"According to the press release, in the phase 3 trial, the participants who got 2-DG had better 'symptom improvement' and spent less time receiving supplemental oxygen. But since we don't know if these two parameters were primary endpoints of the phase 3 trial or just one of the many secondary endpoints, we can't know if the trial was a success or if the release is only reporting the trial's favourable findings. For phase 2, the press release says the researchers reported a "significantly favourable trend": that the vital signs of those who received 2-DG returned to 'normal' 2.5 days sooner on average versus those who didn't receive 2-DG. (We don't know what is 'normal' here either.) There are two problems here. First, normalisation of vital signs is one of the 15 secondary endpoints – not a primary endpoint. There is no information in the release about the primary endpoint nor the other 14 secondary endpoints."*

So as per *The Wire*, normalisation of vital signs are not important?? We are neither doctors nor scientists, but as family members of people who have been affected by the pandemic, some of whom have also lost their lives, we would say that it is absolutely important and therefore not open for discussion.

The scientific genius website continues: *"Second, the words 'significantly favourable' and 'significantly higher' have been used to describe the results of the phase 2 and 3 results. The phrase 'statistically significant' can't be a throwaway term. To be statistically significant means a particular measurement is too large to be the result of chance. And to claim a result is significant in this way, researchers typically perform specific statistical calculations to prove their point. Without seeing these calculations, it's impossible to say if the use of the term 'significantly' in the press release alludes to significance of the statistical variety or the propagandist one. The press release also doesn't use the word 'statistically'."*

Are we more worried about the correctness of the English language of the person who wrote the press release or about the efficacy of the drug itself? *Maybe "The Wire" would have been convinced if Shashi Tharoor wrote the press release!*

The article goes on to say: *"Further, the DCGI relies on the recommendation of the Subject Expert Committee (SEC), a group of independent experts, to grant COVID-related approval. On October 29, 2020, the SEC asked DRL to add 'mortality at 28 days' as one of the efficacy endpoints in the phase 3 trial. But while the press release says the drug was found to be efficacious in the phase 3 trial, it doesn't say anything about the mortality endpoint. Next, a drug's efficacy is only as good as its safety profile. While there have been several human trials for 2-DG over the years, the drug hasn't been approved for human use before this month. According to the CTRI entries, 2-DG's dosage in its phase 2 trial was 45 mg per kg of body weight in the morning and 18 mg/kg in the evening. But in phase 3, this was increased to 45 mg/kg in the morning and 45 mg/kg in the evening – for a total of 90 mg/kg per day. A smaller study by researchers in the US, published in September 2010, tested the drug's effects among 12 cancer patients. They found that 60 mg/kg of 2-DG per day was shown to cause QT prolongation – a severe cardiac condition … that can render the heart beat chaotic in some people. This arrhythmia can in turn lead to a sudden cardiac arrest."*

So *The Wire* **thinks that the DGCI, INMAS–DRDO, DRL, CCMB, and the Modi government have come together to give lakhs (maybe crores) of Indians a heart attack?**

The article continues: *"Another study, published in December 2012, found that ingesting 63-88 mg/kg of 2-DG per day could, among other things, increase the person's blood sugar levels. The press release also doesn't say anything about the drug's safety profile, as ascertained in the phase 2 or phase 3 trials. Phase 3 trials in particular are crucial to understanding any drug's or vaccine's long-term safety. (This is one of the reasons the DCGI's approval for Covaxin without any data from its phase 3 trial proved so controversial.) And of course, it's impossible to discover any rare side-effects in a trial with only 220 participants; tens of thousands had to have been enrolled instead."*

More than 2.02 crore doses of Covaxin have already been administered over a period of four months—does *The Wire* have a count of how many of those people died due to the vaccine?

"*There is minimal information about how the trials were conducted, as there is no data or publication in the public domain. This is not a new or proprietary molecule, and this is publicly funded research. The data should be in the public domain,*" said Dr Sahaj Rathi of the Institute of Liver and Biliary Sciences, Delhi.

This is the only point that we agree with and Amit had sent out this tweet about six hours before he read *The Wire* article.

We are not surprised that Arnab Goswami of *Republic* TV calls this website "The Liar", despite his obvious pro-Modi and pro-Modi bias.

On another note, the government needs to instruct the Intelligence Bureau or the National Investigation Agency or the CBI to investigate whether any funding comes to *The Wire* from any of India's enemies/ rivals such as China, Pakistan, or the USA's CIA-funded 'think-tanks'.

The DRDO also developed a COVID-19 antibody detection kit called "Dipcovan". This kit can detect spike as well as nucleocapsid (S&N) proteins of the SARS-CoV-2 virus.

Armed Forces Mobilized

Apart from developing the 2-DG drug, the DRDO and HAL (Hindustan Aeronautics Ltd.) within a period of 50 days added over 7,000 beds in temporarily–built or existing hospitals in the country, with the help of state governments and the Armed Forces, and in some cases even universities.

DRDO is not the only organization within the Ministry of Defence that helped India to fight the war against COVID-19.

The IAF (Indian Air Force) was mobilised for airlifting cryogenic tankers from the UAE, Singapore, and other countries. They were also airlifting tankers within India by C–17 and C–130 transport aircraft. Till May 27, the IAF carried out 168 international sorties (>3.52 lakh air miles) and 1,443 domestic sorties (>8.89 lakh air miles).

Seven warships of the Indian Navy were deployed for bringing liquid medical oxygen-filled cryogenic containers and associated medical equipment from various countries.

On April 26, all health facilities of Defence PSUs and Ordnance Factory Board were allowed to provide health services to COVID-19 affected civilians.

On the same day, the Chief of Defence Staff (CDS) briefed the PM that all medical personnel from the Armed Forces who have retired or taken premature retirement in the last two years are being recalled to work in COVID-19 facilities within proximity of their residence. Other medical officers who retired earlier have also been requested to make their services available for consultation through medical emergency helplines. All medical officers on staff appointments at Command HQ, Corps HQ, Division HQ and similar HQs of Navy and Air-Force would be employed at hospitals. The CDS informed the PM that nurses are being employed in large numbers to complement the doctors at the hospitals. Oxygen cylinders available with the forces in various establishments were to be released for hospitals. The CDS also said that the forces are creating medical facilities in large numbers and where possible, military medical infrastructure will be made available to civilians. The PM also discussed with the CDS that Kendriya and Rajya Sainik Welfare Boards and officers posted in various headquarters in veterans cells may be instructed to coordinate the services of veterans to extend the reach to maximum extent possible, including in remote areas.

Since there was an exponential demand for oxygen and oxygen cylinders, and as oxygen was transported in liquid form in cryogenic tanks, quick conversion of liquid oxygen to oxygen gas was a critical challenge faced by all hospitals. Indian Army Engineers put together a task force to find a quick innovation to ensure that oxygen is made available without gas cylinders, obviating the need to refill them frequently. In just seven days, the team, in consultation and support from CSIR and DRDO, put together a working solution. To ensure continuous conversion of liquid oxygen into oxygen gas at the requisite pressure and temperature at the patient's bed, the team used a 250-litre self-pressurizing liquid oxygen cylinder and processed it through a specially designed vaporizer and directly usable outlet pressure with requisite leak-proof pipeline and pressure valves. The team also tested a mobile version to cater for typical shifting requirements in hospitals. The system is economically viable and is safe to operate since it obviates high gas pressure in the pipeline or cylinders and does not require any power supply. This system can be replicated in a quick time frame.

Yes, our Armed Forces are capable of defending India against not just Pakistani terrorists and Chinese PLA soldiers, but also a Chinese bioweapon (covered in detail in a later chapter). But they need approval of the government led by a bold prime minister, as PM Modi had done while ordering the cross-border surgical strikes inside POK in September 2016 (in response to 19 Indian Army personnel being killed at Uri), and the Balakot airstrikes well inside Pakistan (in response to 40 CRPF personnel being killed at Pulwama).

Compare this to the fact that the Sonia-Manmohan Singh Congress/ UPA government did not let the IAF carry out airstrikes on Pak terror training camps (despite the IAF proposing it) after the ghastly 26/11 attacks on Mumbai that resulted in 165+ deaths.

Apart from serving personnel including Armed Forces' doctors and nurses, hundreds of veterans (retired officers and *jawans*) from the forces also came out to help.

Shortage of Hospital Beds
and Ventilators

Yes, India has a shortage of hospital beds, and Amit Bagaria used to say this frequently in several talks and media interviews when his 50:50 joint venture (JV) with an American Fortune 500 company was India's No.1 hospital / healthcare facility development consultancy from 1998 to 2002.

In 2002, Amit's company Asian Health Services produced a joint research study with world-renowned consultants McKinsey, which was presented to Prime Minister Vajpayee. The PM presented the study to Singapore's PM Lee Kuan Yew in April 2002. One of the basic tenets of the study was that India had a huge shortage of hospital beds, and Vajpayee asked Lee how Singapore could help. This led to a JV in November 2003 between India's Apollo Hospitals and Singapore's Parkway Group, which owned the famous Gleneagles Hospital there, to set up a 325-bed hospital in Kolkata. Today, Gleneagles has 2250+ beds in four hospitals in Mumbai, Chennai, Bengaluru, and Hyderabad.

An idea that Amit advocated in 2000 was to develop Birthing Centres (for maternity, gynaecology, foetal medicine, and neonatology). One objective of this was to reduce the load on hospitals, as childbirth is 'wellness', as opposed to being an 'illness'. Apollo set up their first "Cradle" in 2003 and has 14 hospitals across India. Cloud Nine, Birthright, Motherhood, and Fortis have 42 put together.

Look at the Table for hospital beds per 1,000 people in 2017, as per the OECD.

Japan	13.05	China	4.34	Brazil	2.00
Russia	8.05	Turkey	2.81	Mexico	1.38
Germany	8.00	USA	2.77	Indonesia	1.04
France	5.98	UK	2.54	India	0.53

Nothing has changed in the 19 years since 2002. The WHO-recommended minimum at that time was 3.2 beds per 1,000 people, which has now come down to 2.9–3.0 per 1,000, because advancements in medicine and surgery now require shorter hospital stays, which Amit had already predicted 19–21 years back. Even if we take the lower number of 2.9, **India only has 18.3% of the minimum hospital beds required**.

This has not happened because of Modi or the BJP. All governments since 1947, including Modi's, must share the blame, in proportion to the years they were in power. This means that the Congress gets 77.7% of the blame, while the BJP gets 17.9%. We are making facts clear, as a huge portion of Indians do not even know who was/is in power for how long in the 73.75 years since Independence.

Look at the Statista graphic here for critical care beds (ICU beds) per one lakh people in 10 countries. The data for Asian countries is from 2017, when Modi had been PM for just three years. Congress or Congress-supported governments were in power for 57.3 years out of 70 years till 2017.

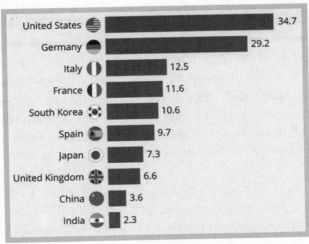

How about tertiary-care referral hospitals, also known in India as 'super-specialty' hospitals? Let's look at AIIMS, probably the finest teaching and tertiary-care hospitals in the public sector.

Rajkumari Amrit Kaur, the princess of Kapurthala (Lucknow), was India's first health minister in the Nehru government, and the first Asian woman to head a WHO governing body. She was the woman behind the first AIIMS in Delhi, which was announced in 1952 and opened in 1956. What happened after that?

City	State	Announced	PM	Opened or Target	Ph-1 Completed By
Jodhpur	Rajasthan	Aug 2003	Vajpayee	Sep 2013	Sonia Government
Bhubaneswar	Odisha	Aug 2003	Vajpayee	Feb 2014	Sonia Government
Raipur	Chhattisgarh	Aug 2003	Vajpayee	Feb 2014	Sonia Government
Rishikesh	Uttarakhand	Aug 2003	Vajpayee	Feb 2014	Sonia Government
Bhopal	MP	Aug 2003	Vajpayee	Aug 2014	Modi Government
Patna	Bihar	Aug 2003	Vajpayee	May 2018	Modi Government
Raebareli	UP	Feb 2009	Dr Singh	July 2018	Modi Government
Gorakhpur	UP	July 2014	Modi	Feb 2019	Modi Government
Mangalagiri	Andhra Pr.	July 2014	Modi	Mar 2019	Modi Government
Nagpur	Maharashtra	July 2014	Modi	July 2019	Modi Government
Kalyani	West Bengal	July 2014	Modi	Oct 2021	Modi Government
Darbhanga	Bihar	Feb 2015	Modi	Sep 2019	Modi Government
Bathinda	Punjab	Feb 2015	Modi	Dec 2019	Modi Government
Guwahati	Assam	Feb 2015	Modi	Aug 2021	Modi Government
Vijaypur	J&K (Jammu)	Feb 2015	Modi	June 2023	Modi Government
Bilaspur	Himachal Pr.	Feb 2015	Modi	Jan 2022	Modi Government
Madurai	Tamil Nadu	Feb 2015	Modi	Under Construction	NA
Bibinagar	Telangana	Feb 2017	Modi	June 2020	Modi Government
Deoghar	Jharkhand	Feb 2017	Modi	Under Construction	NA
Rajkot	Gujarat	Feb 2017	Modi	Under Construction	NA
Manethi	Haryana	Feb 2019	Modi	Under Construction	NA

It took us more than four hours to research all the above information one hospital at a time as almost all of the data on Wikipedia is wrong.

In most cases, the Phase-1 completion (Month Opened) only indicates the opening of the OPD (Outpatient Department) of the hospitals, and does not mean that inpatients were being admitted on those dates (months) or any major treatments such as surgeries being performed.

As you can see, no Congress government from 1956 to 1998 announced or developed a single AIIMS. The first BJP prime minister, Atal Bihari Vajpayee, announced six AIIMS but the government changed and the Congress-led United Progressive Alliance (UPA) came to power. The UPA hurriedly opened OPDs in four of these six AIIMS hospitals just before the 2014 Lok Sabha elections. The other two were completed after the Modi government came to power in May 2014. During 10 years of UPA rule, only one AIIMS was announced, in Sonia Gandhi's constituency Raebareli (UP), and even that was not built. The Modi government ensured its completion.

Within two months of becoming PM, Modi announced four AIIMS, and all are operational. Six more AIIMS were announced seven months later, and three are operational.

The Modi Sarkar has sanctioned 14 of the 22 total AIIMS. Both BJP prime ministers combined have planned 20 of the 22 AIIMS operating or under construction so far, in 13 years, compared with just two being planned by Congress governments in 57.2 years.

And Congress tweets rubbish about Modi's policies and actions multiple times a day using hashtags like #ModiGovtSeNaHoPayega, #ResignModi, #FailedPMModi, #ModiMustResign, etc. etc.

On April 21, 2020 India had 62,458 oxygen-supported hospital beds; this increased to 2,55,168 by April 9, 2021. ICU beds were increased from 27,360 to 75,867 during the same period.

The GOI added 2,105 beds in Delhi alone between March 20 and May 5, 2021, in GOI–owned hospitals. About 70,000 isolation beds were made available by Indian Railways in more than 4,400 Covid-care coaches at 17 locations in seven states.

Delhi's Kejriwal government spent ₹47,634 crores on health from April 2015 to March 2021, but not a single hospital bed or ventilator or oxygen plant was added. AAP's 2015 election manifesto had said they will create 30,000 beds in Delhi hospitals. Now the excuse is that there is no land available. Why do we need 206 acres of samadhis for six former PMs and a former President when Gandhiji is happy with 5.1 acres and former PM Vajpayee with 1.5 acres? Take 175 acres away and Delhi can build a medicity (like it's aerocity) with multiple hospitals having over 13,500 beds. That equals 20 hospitals of the average size of Indraprastha Apollo, Sir Gangaram and BLK Super Speciality Hospital *(which by the way was planned and designed by Amit's company in 1999-2002).*

Defence Minister Rajnath Singh got the DRDO to add more than 7,000 beds in temporarily–built or existing hospitals in the country, with the help of the Armed Forces, and in some cases even universities, in record time of less than 60 days on an average.

On the subject of ventilators again there has been a lot of controversy. No serious shortage was felt during the first wave of COVID-19. If such high numbers of the second wave were not predicted by anyone, how would India have enough ventilators?

In any case, the availability of ventilators in government hospitals was increased by the Modi government by 3.45 times, from 17,850 ventilators in April 2020 (average 245 per year since Independence) to 76,700 by April 2021. Of the 58,850 "Make in India" ventilators added in just a year (>76.7% of total) at around 10% of the cost of foreign-made ones, 50,000 were funded by the PM CARES Fund.

There was gross negligence in many states in operationalizing these ventilators (see *Times of India* report in on the left side of the pic). Congress-ruled Punjab (pic on top right), Chhattisgarh (pic on bottom right), and Rajasthan, as well as BJP-ruled Karnataka and Bihar were the biggest culprits.

A government hospital in Congress-ruled Rajasthan leased out 20 of the ventilators it had received from the GOI, to a private hospital, giving the excuse that they were not working. They miraculously started working at the private hospital, which made huge profits by charging high rates for their usage. How much of this came back as kickback to Congress ministers?

We^2 Need O$_2$

Why did India face a huge oxygen shortage? Demand shot up from just 900 MTPD (metric tons per day) before the second wave to over 7,000 MTPD by April 28. Many patients consumed more oxygen than they needed. Co-vultures stored oxygen to create an artificial shortage. A cylinder can cater to up to four patients at a hospital, but when a person takes it home, he three others of oxygen.

The PM CARES Fund (PMCF) on Jan 5, 2021, allocated ₹201.58 crores for 162 PSA oxygen plants with a capacity of 154.19 MTPD. Only 33 were built in 102 days, though it takes <45 days to build one. Here is the performance of the states, from the best to the worst.

STATE	RULING PARTY	No. Allocated	No. Built	% Built
Chandigarh	BJP	3	3	100.0%
Madhya Pradesh	BJP	8	5	62.5%
Himachal Pradesh	BJP	7	4	57.1%
Uttarakhand	BJP	7	3	42.9%
Bihar	BJP (NDA)	5	2	40.0%
Telangana	TRS (Opposition)	5	2	40.0%
Gujarat	BJP	8	3	37.5%
Karnataka	BJP	6	2	33.3%
Punjab	Congress	3	1	33.3%
Chhattisgarh	Congress	4	1	25.0%
Kerala	Left (Opposition)	5	1	20.0%
Andhra Pradesh	YSRCP (Unaligned)	5	1	20.0%
Haryana	BJP	6	1	16.7%
Puducherry	Congress	6	1	16.7%
Delhi	AAP (Opposition)	8	1	12.5%
Maharashtra	Congress & Allies	10	1	10.0%
Uttar Pradesh	BJP	14	1	7.1%
Odisha	BJD (Unaligned)	7	1	14.3%
Mizoram and Sikkim	BJP & Allies	1	0	0.0%
Tripura, Goa and Lakshadweep	BJP	2	0	0.0%
Ladakh, Manipur, Meghalaya, Nagaland	BJP & Allies	3	0	0.0%
Rajasthan & Jharkhand	Congress & Allies	4	0	0.0%
West Bengal	TMC (Opposition)	5	0	0.0%
Assam and J&K	BJP	6	0	0.0%

The numbers tell the story, don't they? The BJP did well in some states, but failed in UP, Haryana, and many small states. Assam had prior to the PMCF sanction already installed eight plants with a capacity of 5.25 MTPD. But you can see how badly Congress and its allies, Mamata Banerjee, and Arvind Kejriwal did, and they made the maximum noise about the shortage of oxygen.

Delhi witnessed the highest number of deaths due to lack of oxygen. As per a reply to an RTI query, the **Kejriwal government spent about ₹505 crores from January 2020 to March 2021 on advertisements and publicity. At ₹1.244 crores per PSA oxygen plant, it could have built 406 PSA oxygen plants which could have generated 386.4 MTPD, thereby ensuring that people in Delhi did not die for want of oxygen.**

Compare Kejriwal's ₹33.67 crores average monthly expenditure on publicity with ₹25-33 crores of Coke and Oppo; ₹21-29 crores of Samsung, Pepsi, LIC, Amul, PhonePe, Asian Paints, and Vodafone; and ₹13-21 crores of Tata Motors, Hyundai, Airtel, Honda, Dabur, TVS Motors, Bajaj Auto, Britannia, and Emami; and you will understand how much this man is spending. Who is the only 'star' in AAP's ads? None other than Arvind Kejriwal. Have you ever wondered why the chief minister of one state needs to advertise himself nationally? It's not AAP that spends the money, but the Delhi Govt. **Yes, this huge amount being spent on one man's publicity is public (taxpayer) money.**

Leading oxygen producer INOX wrote to Delhi Govt. on April 24 that while the Centre had directed it on April 21 to supply 105 MTPD to 45 Delhi hospitals, the Delhi Govt. on April 23 asked it to supply 98 MTPD to only 17 hospitals. INOX asked the Kejriwal government to clarify if other gas suppliers would cater the requirements of the other hospitals with which INOX had a contract. This was another clear case of mismanagement by the Kejriwal government.

When Delhi had 89,592 active COVID-19 cases on May 3, it demanded 976 MT. Mumbai, which had 84,743 active cases on April 20, used only 245 MT. Why did Delhi need 3.77 times more oxygen than Mumbai? With 2.58% of the country's active cases, Delhi was demanding 11.36% of the nation's oxygen supply. **What was Kejriwal doing with the excess gas?**

Even the Delhi High Court came down strongly on his government regarding mismanagement of oxygen distribution. They said that if the Delhi Govt. is short of resources or unable to handle the situation, they should call the Army for help. But if Kejriwal called in the Army to help, the problem would get solved—that's not what he wanted, did he?

The maximum SOS tweets and WhatsApp messages for oxygen were coming from Delhi. They were also coming from private hospitals (some of their directors were also giving TV interviews), and we have already spoken about their being hands-in-glove with the AMB in an earlier chapter. As soon as a Supreme Court-appointed task force recommended to order an oxygen audit of states, over 90% of these SOS tweets and messages stopped, **as if Delhi suddenly had no oxygen shortage anymore**.

It is amusing that Kejriwal had earlier claimed that AAP will set up an oxygen testing centre in every city and village of India.

Not a single mainstream media organization questioned Kejriwal for his incompetence and inefficiency in handling the oxygen crisis—that's the true power of the advertisement money.

After Delhi's 'supposed' oxygen crisis was over, Kejriwal started a new drama about Delhi having a shortage of vaccines. Kejriwal and his ministers started talking about a 'supposed' vaccine shortage in Delhi in the second half of April. On April 30, Delhi had ~4.83 lakh doses available, and was supplied another 3.5+ lakh doses in the first week of May. Yet, less than 4.95 lakh jabs were given to people in the first week of May. People were reluctant to go for vaccination because Kejriwal's and AAP ministers' statements made them believe there was a shortage.

As if that was not enough, he tweeted on May 18 that the GOI should ban flights from Singapore because Indian children could get affected in a 'third wave' by a Singapore-strain of the Coronavirus. Why not Mr Kejriwal, a country with average 34 cases per day would cause a third wave in a country of 139 crore people. Singapore had already banned flights from India more than 25 days prior to Kejriwal's statement. The country's foreign ministry said that it reserved the right to invoke a domestic law on the online circulation of fake news against Kejriwal for his tweet about a COVID-19 variant demonstrating more ferocity in infecting children in Singapore.

Before this goof up, Kejriwal had been the target of the most malicious tweets after Modi himself. His 'Singapore Sling' made him the brunt of hundreds of jokes. This tweet by JNU scientist and professor Dr Anand Ranganathan, who is a well-known Twitter and TV personality, got 3,802 retweets/replies and 19,500 likes in just two hours.

Coming back to oxygen, on April 24, the PMCF sanctioned an additional 389 PSA oxygen plants. The entire cost of all these 551 oxygen plants, including seven years' maintenance, is borne by the GOI. The PMCF also sanctioned one lakh portable oxygen concentrators. Earlier, the PMCF had also approved procurement of 1.5 lakh units of SpO2 based oxygen supply system developed by DRDO. In addition, it was announced on April 28 that the DRDO will set up 500 medical oxygen plants within three months with funds provided by the PMCF.

Customs duty and health cess was removed on oxygen and oxygen-related equipment by the GOI. It also directed all major ports to waive all charges for ships carrying oxygen and related equipment.

The GOI ensured that production was increased by 65.6% in just 31 days, from 5,700 MTPD on April 10 to over 9,440 MTPD on May 11, which was more than the country's daily needs that day. More than a year ago, the GOI had allowed manufacturers of industrial oxygen to produce and sell medical oxygen. As a result, 28 units located in major steel plants were supplying around 1,500 MTPD.

But the main problem continued to be transportation/logistics, as most oxygen plants are located far from where the major requirements were. State governments are responsible for picking up supplies and deliver to hospitals, but most state governments pathetically failed in this task, leading to an extra 25-30% deaths which should not have happened.

Kejriwal, Uddhav Thackeray, and some other opposition CMs kept blaming the Centre for the oxygen crisis. On the other hand, Mumbai's municipal commissioner said that his emergency call to the Cabinet Secretary of India was answered in 15-20 seconds and oxygen was dispatched the same evening. He said the GOI should not be blamed at all for the oxygen shortage, and if anyone is to be blamed, it is the states.

India was not the only country or Delhi the only major global city that faced an oxygen crisis. This January 6, 2021, article said that "*Los Angeles County has been so overwhelmed it is running out of oxygen, with ambulance crews instructed to use oxygen only for their worst-case patients. They were **told not to bring patients to the hospital if they have little hope of survival and to treat and declare such patients dead on the scene to preserve hospital capacity.***"

A post by Hanuman Mal Bengani, former CEO of Linde India, one of India's largest oxygen producers, was being circulated on **April 26** [Note: We have not corrected his grammar]: "*Having spent 45 years in oxygen industry and involved with setting up 50% of production capacities in India I can share few facts: (1) Industrial and medical oxygen are same product produced in same plant, stored in same tanks and filled in same cylinders. For medical oxygen the gas company have to analyse and certify each batch. No other difference. In fact, for industrial we need 99.5% pure oxygen; whereas for medical all over the world is 93 +/- 3%; (2) **There is absolutely no shortage of oxygen in India. Less than 1% of oxygen capacity is used for medical purposes.** Even in corona times it may go up to three times or even five but that's it; (3) I estimate total production capacity to be around 100,000 MTPD (or may be more) and around 80% are with steel companies. Reliance Jamnagar has 22,000 MTPD capacity for petcoke gasification; (4) Most captive plants are in East India, some in the West (Mumbai and Gujarat) and some in Karnataka. These plants typically produce 5-10% of the product as liquid which is stored in large tanks. This liquid is used as back up when plant is down and to meet peak demands; (5) There are several standalone liquid oxygen plants owned by gas companies like Linde and Inox where they produce liquid oxygen and sell to various customers through tankers and tanks; (6) Several re-fillers around the country buy liquid from gas companies and fill gas cylinders after vaporising liquid oxygen; (7) Oxygen is generally delivered to end user by three means: 80% through pipeline from plant to end user, 15% or so in liquid form through tanks and tankers, and <5% through cylinders.*

*"**So why are we facing crisis today?** I think combination of following: (1) Shortage of distribution assets, i.e., road tankers, storage tanks and cylinders. These are expensive. Each road tanker costs ₹45 lakhs and a cylinder costs around ₹10,000 in which you sell oxygen just worth ₹300. These assets have been built by gas companies based on normal times. There is only that much one can do with these assets; (2) Most plants are located in select geographies. So distribution assets travel fair distance (200-1000 kms) to deliver to customer. Now even with good roads a tanker takes 7-10 days to make a round trip and a cylinder also takes that much turn around; (3) Desire of gas companies to focus on what maximises their profits; (4) Last but not least this wave came so quick it took our government administration with pants down. Had they thought of this impending danger and prepared, a major crisis could have been avoided.*

"But that's easier said than done knowing our democratic set up. Now Govt. is taking steps. In hindsight I think Govt. could have planned following things: (1) Strict advisory to gas companies to use all distribution assets for medical purpose only from day one. They could provide compensation to gas companies for this just like MSP for food grains; (2) Advise all captive plants owners not to use a drop of liquid oxygen from plant / tank for their process use until they are full; (3) Using rails to transport through green door track; (4) All hospitals could have installed PSA captive plants. PMO had announced ₹200 crores for all district hospitals and they could have around 500 plants. In usual public sector tendering process not even 15% of that has been used; (5) CEOs of large hospitals are also equally responsible. When they charge such huge money from public, they should have better prepared themselves. What FOR are they getting fat salaries and bonuses? Once this crisis is over I think some heads of CEO of large hospitals must roll."

Let's do a fact check on whether the Modi Sarkar took the five steps advised by Mr Bengani:

(1) On April 18 (a Sunday, and eight days before Mr Bengani's note) the Union Home Secretary wrote to Chief Secretaries of all states, asking them to prohibit oxygen supply for industrial use, except nine specified exempted industries;

(2) On April 25 (again a Sunday and a day before Mr Bengani's note), the GOI imposed a blanket ban, removing the earlier exemption for nine industries;

(3) On April 17, Minister of Railways Piyush Goyal had already told the Railways to transport LMO (liquid medical oxygen) in cryogenic tankers and oxygen cylinders on "Oxygen Express" trains running on green corridors (railway tracks on which other traffic is stopped/diverted to allow these trains to pass); As of May 23, almost 15,000 MT of oxygen had been delivered by 234 Oxygen Express trains;

(4) We have already covered this point as far as government hospitals are concerned and yes, private hospitals should have done it—it should now be made into a law!

(5) Like we have said before …

Remdesivir & Plasma

The ICMR has failed to update the treatment protocol for COVID-19 since July 2020. As the western world updated its treatment protocols with emerging evidence, **Indian patients were being prescribed Remdisivir, even 10 months after it was no longer recommended by the WHO**.

India's health ministry issued its last treatment protocol on 3 July 2020, which listed Remdesivir as part of "investigational therapies" that would be upgraded "as the situation evolves, and when more data becomes available."

In November 2020, WHO said that it *"recommends against the use of Remdesivir in COVID-19 patients."* The statement noted, *"WHO has issued a conditional recommendation against the use of Remdesivir in hospitalized patients, regardless of disease severity, as there is currently no evidence that Remdesivir improves survival and other outcomes in these patients."*

But the health ministry's treatment protocol was not updated, and private hospitals across the nation have continued to prescribe it at exorbitant costs. The ICMR's failure to update the treatment guidelines in line with global standards have also resulted in a thriving black market for Remdesivir that continues to prey on vulnerable families.

Some of India's leading doctors have said that 85% of COVID-19 patients do not require steroids or Remdesivir, yet, more than 70% were being prescribed these treatments.

In any case, because of the huge demand, the GOI managed to get pharma companies to not only almost treble India's Remdesivir production to ~1.05 crore vials per month within 23 days (April 12 to May 4), but also convinced them to drop prices by 50-70%.

The same was the case with plasma therapy. On May 17, 2021, the ICMR finally dropped plasma therapy from its clinical management guidelines for the disease. Back in September 2020, ICMR's own study had found that the therapy was not associated with stopping patients from becoming severely ill or reducing mortality (death). Several studies around the world had reported similar findings.

Clearly, these shortages were created for no reason, as most of these treatments are not required in a vast majority of COVID-19 patients.

Modi Did Nothing!

Yes, it is an opposition politician's job to oppose the government of the day and the ruling party, but this job has to take a break when there is a national crisis of any sort, as we have said at the beginning of this book. At times of national crisis—be it a war or a pandemic or an economic depression or anything else that affects a large part of a nation's population—politics of any kind has to stop, and politicians of all hues need to come together to work as one.

Far from that happening during the COVID-19 pandemic in India, especially in the second wave, opposition politicians took on Modi and his government as well the BJP like there was no tomorrow! As if Modi and the BJP purposely caused the second wave. If that was not enough, opposition politicians and even members of the anti-Modi media (more about them later) even took on Modi's religion—Hinduism—as if Hindus had caused the second wave. This led to a social media war never-seen-before in India.

There were at least two videos on Twitter where Muslims were saying on loudspeakers (one was a live event with almost no one wearing masks and no social distancing and the other was a recording being played over a loudspeaker mounted on a small truck) that constructing the Ram Mandir in Ayodhya was causing COVID-19, as Allah was punishing the infidels. Was this in retaliation to the lakhs of Hindus targeting the Tablighi Jamaat in April 2020 for becoming the biggest super-spreader gathering just as the first wave was underway? Even if it was, does it make it right?

Apart from the shortage of beds, oxygen, vaccines, and treatment drugs, that we have already covered, most of the blame targeted towards

Modi and the BJP was on four issues: (1) Modi and senior ministers were too busy in campaigning for assembly elections in West Bengal, Tamil Nadu, Kerala, and Assam, and therefore ignored the impending second wave; (2) The elections and the Kumbh Mela in Haridwar were the biggest 'super-spreader' events; (3) Instead of using money towards COVID-relief, Modi diverted it for the Central Vista project; and (4) The money in the PM CARES Fund was not used to fight the pandemic. We shall cover all of these points, except the Kumbh Mela, which we have already said should have not been held.

Consider a fact—the same Modi was praised—both within India and globally—for his 'efficient' handling of the pandemic during the first phase. As per the chart at the end of the chapter "Was the Second Wave Planned?", Modi's 'approval rating' was at an all-time high of 83-84% during the 51-day national lockdown. He had the highest approval rating amongst leaders of the 13 biggest economies in the world (except China and Russia, where people don't dare speak up against Jinping or Putin), and his rating had gone up by 12% in just 36 days.

This was mainly because he declared a 21-day national lockdown on March 24, 2020, when India had only reported 536 cumulative COVID-19 cases, and the maximum in a single day was only 103. On April 14 (cumulative cases 10,453; single-day peak 1248), Modi declared Lockdown 2.0 for two more weeks. On May 1 (cumulative cases 34,863; single-day peak 1873), he extended the national lockdown for another two weeks. On May 17 (cumulative cases 90,648; single-day peak 4864), the lockdown was extended for a third time, for another two weeks. Effectively, the world's second-most populous country had a total lockdown for 51 days from March 25 to May 31, 2020.

Modi's approval ratings fell to 63-68% between April 23 and May 18, 2021, at the peak of the second wave. Yet, at 64% on May 18, just 13 days after the peak of the second wave, Modi remained the highest-rated leader, ahead of the PMs/Presidents of the US, Japan, Germany, the UK, France, Italy, Canada, South Korea, Australia, Brazil, Spain, and Mexico.

After that, there were no more 'national' lockdowns. This was because Modi was criticised very severely by opposition parties (even though their state chief ministers had supported the lockdowns), the media, the business community, migrant labour who had lost their jobs, daily-wage earners who had also lost their jobs, and of course, the Twitterati, which included many real economists and other 'armchair experts'.

Just look at the timeline in the graph below. Does it make sense to you that a chief executive of any democracy will impose nationwide lockdowns when peak daily cases were 103, or 1248, or 1873, or 4864, but not do the same when cases shot up to over 1,50,000 on April 10, 2021?

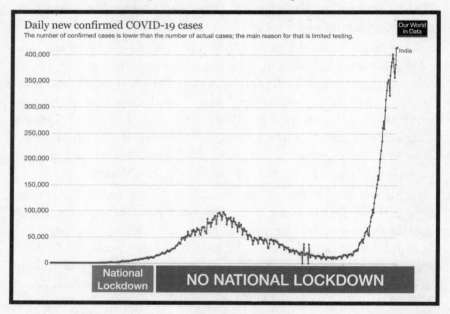

The problem is, you just cannot satisfy everyone. **Modi had come in for harsh criticism by over 90% of the population for 'screwing up' the economy during the 2020 lockdown**. Apart from Rahul Gandhi and many other politicians, he was mocked by the Indian media and the intelligentsia.

Modi wisely left it to state governments to decide whether they wanted lockdowns in their states. Most CMs were forced to impose lockdowns in their whole states or within certain areas, some even having to extend the lockdowns up to four times, some extending beyond the 51-day national lockdown of 2020. Of course, Mamata *didi* declared a lockdown only after Ramzan was over, and even then, saree shops and jewellery shops were allowed to function within restricted hours.

Ironically, the same people who criticized Modi for the 2020 lockdown imposed lockdowns themselves in 2021. This time, most of the Leftist media (which is a majority in Indian media) kept quiet. After all, their problem is not with Rahul or Kejriwal or Uddhav Thackeray, etc., they only have a problem with Modi, the BJP, or the RSS.

In a *ABP News*-CVoter poll of 1.39 lakh people in all 543 Lok Sabha constituencies which concluded on May 28, 2021, of those who did not answer 'Don't Know/Can't Say', 75.2% said Modi was correct in imposing a national lockdown in 2020, and 61.7% said Modi's 2021 decision of not imposing a national lockdown was correct.

Except the Kumbh Mela, let us closely examine the three other reasons for which Modi and his government have been blamed.

Firstly, were Modi and his ministers too busy campaigning for elections, and did they therefore ignore the gravity of the second wave? Was Modi sleeping, without bothering about the precious lives of Indian citizens? Isn't Modi an astute politician? Isn't he interested in winning elections? Isn't that the goal of every politician, regardless of his or her party? How can Modi win any election—leave alone get re-elected as PM in 2024—if he ignores citizens and lets them die? Isn't he smart enough to understand something as basic as this?

STATE	CASES	Population	Cases/Lakh
Kerala	4,958	3,62,73,000	13.7
Maharashtra	3,442	12,58,37,000	2.7
West Bengal	1,116	10,16,92,000	1.1
Chhattisgarh	1,028	3,04,09,000	3.4
Tamil Nadu	936	7,92,65,000	1.2
Uttar Pradesh	907	24,74,00,000	0.4
Karnataka	843	6,91,80,000	1.2
Madhya Pradesh	837	8,85,42,000	0.9
Gujarat	788	6,47,30,000	1.2
Rajasthan	672	8,41,54,000	0.8
Delhi	624	1,91,92,000	3.3
Bihar	459	12,99,75,000	0.4
Telangana	388	4,04,53,000	1.0
Haryana	333	2,89,18,000	1.2
Uttarakhand	332	1,15,42,000	2.9
Punjab	269	3,07,41,000	0.9
J&K	214	1,39,43,000	1.5

The allegation of not taking any action is completely baseless. On January 7, 2021, when there were only 18,380 ADCs (average daily cases) in all of India during the past week (18.8% of the first wave peak), the Union Health Secretary wrote to Kerala, Maharashtra, Chhattisgarh, and West Bengal, *"urging them to take prompt steps and keep a 'strict vigil' to curb recent spikes in cases. The states were advised against any laxity which may squander the results gained so far."*

The previous Table shows average daily cases in 17 states in the preceding two weeks. We have not included any other states as their numbers were very low. It seems the people in the MoHFW sent the letter to the four 'chosen states' based purely on the average cases in the preceding two weeks being above 1,000, and not any other criteria. There was clearly a major flaw. They should have looked at cases per lakh and should have therefore sent the letter to Delhi and Uttarakhand instead of West Bengal. There should be an inquiry into why Delhi and Uttarakhand were excluded, and why Bengal was included. The other three states were correctly chosen, whether 'wisely' or by sheer luck.

On February 25, when the ADCs had fallen to 13,779 (14.1% of the first wave peak), the Cabinet Secretary (India's senior-most bureaucrat) scheduled a review meeting with seven states—Maharashtra, Kerala, Punjab, MP, Tamil Nadu, Gujarat, and Chhattisgarh, which had 'supposedly' witnessed an upsurge in cases. In addition, 'multi-disciplinary high level central teams' (whatever that means) were rushed to states and UTs witnessing spikes. We are not sure whether it were the same seven, as there is no UT among them.

This Table shows the average daily cases in 12 states in the preceding two weeks. Once again, it seems the criteria was the highest absolute number of cases, instead of cases per lakh. But why was Karnataka left out? And once again, Delhi should

STATE	CASES	Population	Cases/Lakh
Maharashtra	4,919	12,58,37,000	3.9
Kerala	4,403	3,62,73,000	12.1
Tamil Nadu	458	7,92,65,000	0.6
Karnataka	396	6,91,80,000	0.6
Punjab	326	3,07,41,000	1.1
Gujarat	284	6,47,30,000	0.4
Chhattisgarh	263	3,04,09,000	0.9
Madhya Pradesh	243	8,85,42,000	0.3
West Bengal	178	10,16,92,000	0.2
Telangana	148	4,04,53,000	0.4
Delhi	142	1,91,92,000	0.7
J&K	74	1,39,43,000	0.5

have been included, instead of Gujarat and MP. Was the GOI trying to prove they were being equally harsh on BJP/NDA ruled states?

Apart from these warnings given by the MoHFW and the Cabinet Secretary, Modi had six virtual meetings with all state CMs—on January 11 (ADCs 18,020), March 8 (ADCs 16,745), March 17 (ADCs 25,138), April 8 (ADCs 1,00,765), April 14 (ADCs 1,53,113), and April 23 (ADCs 2,81,379)—only to discuss COVID-19. Though she was invited to all the meetings, Mamata Banerjee did not attend a single one.

The prime minister used to hold such meetings on a regular basis during the first wave also. His first three meetings in 2021 were held well before the second wave started, when COVID-19 cases were just 4.35%, 4.04%, and 6.07% of the second-wave peak. Five of the meetings were held within 46 days (March 8 to April 23) and all of these were held during the election campaign.

Cases went up 13.2 times from March 17 to April 22. What more can a PM do in 36 days? Personally visit 718 districts at an average of 20 districts a day? Wasn't that the job of the 36 chief ministers, LGs and Administrators? Shouldn't they have taken strong action starting March 10, when it became evident that a second wave was starting?

And where did the second wave start? Maharashtra alone had almost 10.92 lakhs cases between March 10 and April 10, which was 52.74% of the cases in all of India. The state is ruled by a 3-party alliance which includes the Congress party. Why did this happen?

Because Bollywood stars and fashion models had **started partying heavily** once more. Joining the party was the city's tens of thousands of millionaires and lakhs of other investors who had made a killing from the stock market, which had risen over 31.5% in just three and a half months and 54.5% in eight months. In December and January, many of them **travelled to countries that were experiencing huge second waves of COVID-19**, and brought back the infection with them. The CM's 31-year-old son, who is the 'tourism' minister, is said to party frequently with this crowd. Need more be said?

Let us now move on to examine if the second wave affected the election-bound states more than other states.

While the graphs below show that the number of cases rose rapidly in Assam, Kerala, and Tamil Nadu after the elections were over, and in West Bengal during the elections, it also shows that **cases rose equally rapidly (if not even more) in at least 12 other states of the other 16 in this chart, where there were no elections**.

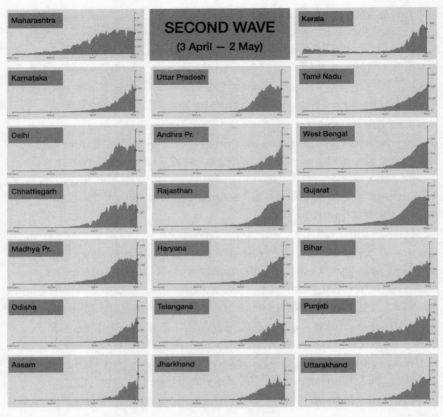

Let us look at another chart, which shows the rise in cases in the 20 most-affected states and the UT of J&K, between March 1 and May 9. The peak cases in each state is not necessarily the daily number recorded on May 9, but the peak number recorded during April/May, the oldest date being in Maharashtra (April 18), followed by Delhi (April 20), Chhattisgarh (April 23), UP (April 24), and MP (April 25), with all other peaks being recorded between April 28 and May 9. The picture becomes even more clear.

Bihar, UP, Andhra Pradesh, Jharkhand, Delhi, and Rajasthan did not have any elections, while Karnataka had bypolls for just three seats. Kerala and Tamil Nadu, which had elections, recorded a much smaller rise than the average of these 20, whereas the rise in West Bengal was also quite low.

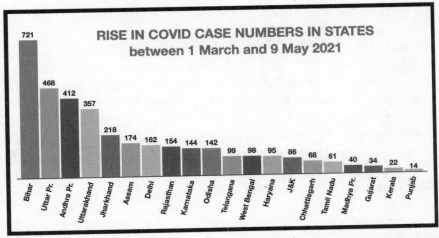

If the sharp rise in Uttarakhand and UP is attributed to the Kumbh Mela, then what explains the highest rise in Bihar, the third highest in Andhra and the fifth highest in Jharkhand?

We shall cover the questions (raised by the AMB) relating to the Central Vista Project and the PM CARES Fund in separate chapters dedicated to each issue.

The "WEST BENGAL COVID-19 HEALTH BULLETIN" dated April 21, 2021 issued by the WB Govt. disclosed these figures. Was this infrastructure adequate to deal with an average of 11,113 cases per day in a 60-day period?

CATEGORY	QUANTITY	PEOPLE PER FACILITY
Total Testing Labs	105	9,68,500
Total Hospitals (Government & Private)	70	14,52,751
Total earmarked Covid-19 Beds	8,194	12,411
Total ICU/HDU Beds in Covid Hospitals	1,838	55,328

If only 15% of the Covid-positive cases in Bengal needed hospitalization and an average length of stay of six days, there would be a 18.1% bed shortage. Does Mamata Banerjee have the right to question the PM on COVID-19? But which journalists question her? They only question Modi, who is the one supposed to be a fascist.

As if all the issues raised by the AMB were not enough, there was another controversy created by the AMB led by the Congress party. With foreign aid pouring in for India starting mid-April 2021 (which we shall cover in a later chapter), around May 3-4, opposition parties questioned the Centre on the whereabouts of the medical supplies received over the past week. The Congress demanded transparency in the distribution of foreign aid and urged PM Modi to make public details of all relief material received by India. *"India has received aid from 40 countries over the past one week. The people of this country have a right to know where the relief material is coming from and where it is going. The government is busy with media management and headline management while people are dying due to shortage of oxygen,"* said Congress spokesperson Pawan Khera.

The truth: 67.2% of ventilators, 46.9% of oxygen concentrators, 55% of oxygen cylinders, and 60.5% of Remdesivir vials received till then, were given to opposition-ruled states which only preside over ~43.4% of India's population.

We have already given you some examples of the massive fake news that was spread nationwide and worldwide by the AMB, especially on Twitter, with the sole purpose of tarnishing Modi's and his government's image. Like we said in the chapter "Was the Second Wave Planned?", there was much, much more…

For example, fake news was spread about the nationalist right-wing organization RSS (considered to be the 'moral' parent body of the BJP) accusing them of not doing for Covid-relief. The truth: in the first wave, 5,07,656 RSS volunteers provided help at 92,656 locations, distributed over 4.66 crore food packets and opened 483 treatment centres.

During the second wave, up to May 12, 2021, more than 3.42 lakh RSS workers had provided *sewa* (assistance) at ~67,000 places, including ~50.5 lakh ration kits and ~3.2 crore meals.

If people still believe Modi and the BJP and the RSS did nothing, we also have a right to ask what the principal opposition party—the Congress—and its main leader, Rahul Gandhi did, apart from tweeting 25-35 times a day and spending crores on defaming the country's duly elected prime minister, and that too a PM who crushed the Congress after demonstrating his vision and governance to the nation for five years.

Apart from the questions we have raised about whether the second wave was planned by the Congress and its partners in crime, and the question that has been raised by crores of Indians about the Congress party's alleged Toolkit, there is no doubt about the fact that the Congress and its leaders are continuously lying and trying to deceive the country from the real truth.

For example, party spokesperson Supriya Shrinate on May 29 said on the *Times Now* TV channel that only 3% of Indians have been vaccinated. The truth: about 17.6% of India's 18+ population had received the first jab, whereas about 4.7% had been fully vaccinated by that day.

She went on to say that Brazil has vaccinated 11% of its population. Even if we consider the total population—which should not be the case as vaccination for <18 has not started—India had vaccinated 3.1% of our total population as of May 28, whereas Brazil was at 10.22%.

So it is convenient for Congress to round down India's number from 3.1% to 3% and at the same time round up Brazil's number from 10.22% to 11%? Besides, India had fully vaccinated 4.409 crore people, which was more than double of Brazil's 2.175 crore. Let us remind you that Brazil's PCGDP is 3.2 times that of India.

There are scores of other examples of the Congress and other opposition parties, as well as other members of the AMB lying and misleading people!

Why Were the Elections
Not Postponed or Cancelled?

In an interview to many leading newspapers on May 8, 2021, India's chief election commissioner (CEC) Sushil Chandra made many important points. Of course, one has to remember he was not CEC when the polls were announced—he was one of the three election commissioners and took over as CEC from Sunil Arora on April 13, 2021, when the elections in Tamil Nadu, Kerala, Assam and Puducherry had finished, but were still going on in West Bengal.

"*Considering the logistics of manpower and central forces' deployment which is decided much in advance, it was not considered necessary to club the last two phases … The COVID guidelines issued on August 21, 2020, worked very well for Bihar polls. When the latest elections were announced in February, Covid situation had significantly improved. There was no indication from the health authorities or experts that a second wave of the pandemic was on its way,*" said Sharma. He was not wrong.

The elections were announced on February 26, when the daily average of cases was 13,045 for the previous two weeks for the whole of India. Compare this to a daily average of 57,108 cases just two months later in Maharashtra alone, and you will get the picture. When the first phase of polling took place in West Bengal and Assam on March 27, West Bengal had an average of 374 daily cases in the previous two weeks, and Assam had just 29 daily cases.

Sharma also said, "*At no point of time in the EC (Election Commission) was there any thought of deferring the elections. Only a request was received for clubbing the last two phases (in West Bengal) and at that time, the EC had discussed various consequences of doing so.*" He was responding to an a 'draft' affidavit that election commissioner Rajiv Kumar had wanted to submit to the Madras High Court (which had harshly criticized the EC), which said the option of deferring some phases was actively considered but shelved as even temporary disenfranchising of voters (stopping them from voting) would cause a hue and cry. Kumar said that the implications of not completing the elections on time, including conducting them later under an extended term (for the sitting government) or President's Rule, might attract sharper criticism of one party being favoured over another.

On April 26, the Madras HC had said, "*Were you (the EC) on another planet when political rallies were being held? You are singularly responsible for the second wave of COVID-19. EC officers should be booked on murder charges probably.*"

Kumar was also not wrong. **There could be only two ways the elections could be postponed—one, extend the terms of the sitting assemblies (and thereby the respective state governments), or two, impose President's Rule.**

If the first option was chosen, the opposition in various states; that is the BJP and the Left–Congress–ISF alliance in West Bengal; the DMK–Congress alliance and the AMMK–DMDK alliance in Tamil Nadu; the Congress–led UDF in Kerala; and the Congress–led alliance in Assam; would have screamed their throats off on TV till the cows came home.

Similarly, if the second option was chosen, the ruling parties/alliances in various states; that is the Trinamool in West Bengal; the AIADMK in Tamil Nadu; the Left Democratic Front in Kerala; and the BJP in Assam; would have done likewise. They would have called in the murder of democracy. Mamata Banerjee would have gone on her life's biggest dharna; she would have called Modi worse names than just Hitler, if there was one.

And postponing two or three phases of elections in Bengal would have resulted in the same thing as the first option; that is, the Mamata government continuing indefinitely. It is a completely different matter that the same government has been re-elected.

UP Chief Minister Yogi Adityanath—who is almost as much hated by the AMB as Modi himself, and even more by some—wanted to postpone the UP Panchayat elections, but the High Court overruled him. About 135 election workers died in UP.

Consider this—when the Modi government suggested at an all–party meeting before the Bihar assembly elections held in October-November 2020 that live public rallies should be banned and there should be only digital campaigning and rallies on apps like Zoom, the opposition, led by the RJD and the Congress, opposed it, saying it would give an unfair advantage to the BJP, which could afford such things. Huh? Aren't virtual campaigns much less expensive that physical election rallies?

They also argued that the concept is *"socially and economically discriminatory [and thus] against the principle of a level-playing field in the democratic exercise"* as virtual campaigns could exclude a large section of the rural people and the poor who have no access to digital connectivity.

While the opposition was not wrong on the second point, what was the EC to do in the case of the March-April 2021 elections? What would you do if you were the sole election commissioner and you alone had to make the decision?

Money for Central Vista
Not for COVID-19

Around May 6, 2021, the Congress party started a campaign against the Central Vista Project (CVP) being developed by the GOVERNMENT OF INDIA in the NATIONAL CAPITAL.

This was not the first time. Opposition started when it was first announced, then when the foundation stone was laid by THE PRIME MINISTER, and again during the first wave of COVID-19. The initial negative articles, published mostly by the anti-Modi media, were based on 'expert' opinions of urban planners and architects who had lost the contest to design the project.

We have capitalized some words above to emphasize the point that the government of the day is building something with several long term benefits for the nation, and it is not an individual or a political party building something for personal gain, as the individual (Modi) or party (BJP) concerned will not be in power permanently.

Does the Congress believe that he/they will, and is that their concern? Or is their concern that they could not do it in 2012 (more about that later). Or that they will not be able to name it Sonia Gandhi Vista, like they named at least 445 medical/educational institutions, roads, buildings, stadiums, airports, ports, sanctuaries, parks, schemes, awards, trophies, tournaments, and fellowships after Nehru, Indira Gandhi, or Rajiv Gandhi?

Let us tell you what the CVP is all about. By 2027, the Government of India will have infrastructure that will be **more modern than any other nation's capital**.

The 919-acre area around the 2.9–km Rajpath from Rashtrapati Bhavan to India Gate is being redeveloped. Existing buildings of 42.6

lakh square feet, some built in the 1960s and 1970s, are being demolished. No heritage building designed by British architect Sir Edward Lutyens is being touched, contrary to misinformation being spread. Several new buildings totalling ~1.89 crore square feet will be built.

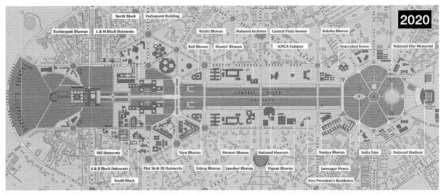

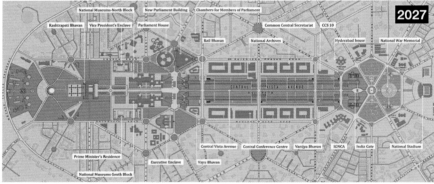

Here are images of the current and the proposed Master Plan of the New Delhi Central Vista. See how the current buildings on the North and South of Rajpath (top Pic)—90% of them built by Congress governments—are of haphazard shapes and sizes, and compare it to how well the new Master Plan is synchronized (bottom Pic).

Currently, there are hundreds of hutments on the South-east of Rashtrapati Bhavan. Most of these will be demolished and replaced with an Executive Enclave for Members of Parliament, as well as for relocating the Indira Gandhi National Centre for the Arts.

Here are two aerial views of the revamped Central Vista, the first being a close-up, and the second from a height. In the first image, Rashtrapati Bhawan can be seen on the top and the National War Memorial as well as India Gate at the bottom. In the second, you can see Connaught Place on the top right.

Although the CVP is budgeted at ₹13,450 crores, having been closely associated with the construction of hospitals for six years and real estate projects for 14 years, Amit estimates that the cost is likely to go up to ₹25,000 crores by the time the project is completed, due to many miscellaneous items not being budgeted as well as cost escalations.

It is very important to keep in mind that this investment (it is <u>not</u> an expenditure) will be spread over seven years, and is not being made only during the COVID-19 pandemic. The only amount being spent from 2020 to August 2022 is ₹1,339 crores.

The first building being constructed is a new four–storey 6.94 lakh square feet triangular **PARLIAMENT HOUSE** (see Pic), 36% larger than the existing 94½ year-old building, with enhanced seating capacities of 888 in the Lok Sabha vs. the current 552 and 384 in the Rajya Sabha vs. the current 245. The new Lok Sabha Hall will accommodate 1,224 MPs for a 'joint' sitting of both the expanded houses.

Of course, the AMB has spread myths that the triangular shape of the building is against the principles of 'Vastu shashtra'. Once again, they 'assume' that Modi is stupid. In regular Vastu, square or rectangular shapes are considered acceptable for buildings. However, when we dive deep into the why the principle came up, we realise they were based of energy flow and movement in the environment with reference to the effect on the human energy field. All shapes have an energy field that can cause effects on the human energy field and can be assessed using various instruments like the Lecher Antenna, the BG3 pendulum, aura photography, GDV camera, etc. On looking at the design of the new Parliament building, though the shape at first glance looks like a triangle, the points have been cut. This creates an angle on all sides. The shape that gets created as a result has been used in BioGeometry principles to create BG3 energies, and can be found in tens of thousands of temples, mosques, churches, and monuments built in the last 4,650+ years. The BG3 energies are very beneficial for us at all levels of consciousness—physical, emotional, mental and spiritual.

Why is a larger Parliament needed? Post–2026, the strength of both houses (Lok Sabha and Rajya Sabha) are mandated to increase to reflect the growth in India's population. This has nothing to do with Modi or the BJP. It is part of the Constitution. The number of Lok Sabha seats were increased ("delimitation") to 494 in 1952 based on the 1951 census, 522 in 1963 based on the 1961 census, and 543 in 1973 based on the 1971 census.

Though there was supposed to be a delimitation exercise every 10 years, this did not happen after 1973. In 2002, through a Constitutional Amendment, it was decided that the next delimitation will be done in 2026 based on the 2021 census.

"If British can have 650 parliamentarians, Canada 443 and the US 535 why can't we have 1000?" asked former President Pranab Mukherjee in December 2019. He was not a BJP politician, but spent most of his career in the Congress.

The existing 94½ year-old building has several structural problems and cannot be expanded to accommodate the growth of both houses. It is already crammed. Very few MPs have offices and MPs of almost all parties have complained about this several times over the years. Besides, there is no space for staff of those MPs who do have offices.

The building is being readied on a war–footing before August 15, 2022, to coincide with the 75th anniversary of India's Independence; hence it cannot be delayed.

Features in the Lok Sabha and Rajya Sabha halls will include a desk in every MP's seat (currently available only in front rows), enough space behind seats for free movement, a touchscreen-based digital voting system, biometric-based dual authentication, and an intuitive multilingual graphical user interface.

There will be a Constitution Hall, which visitors can access, to understand India's journey as a parliamentary democracy. There will also be a lounge and a dining room for MPs, a library, multiple committee rooms, and 1,100 car parks. Each MP will have a 430 square feet office with space for staff.

The new Parliament building is being built by Tata Projects at a cost of ₹862 crores. Neither is it going to be enjoyed by just the BJP and its allies (MPs of all parties will get the benefit) nor is the BJP going to be in power permanently.

A **CENTRAL VISTA AVENUE** (see Pics), with bridges over canals, pedestrian underpasses, wide footpaths, more green areas than now, benches for seating, and tree-shaded public parking spaces, is being built by Shapoorji Pallonji at a cost of ₹477 crores. This is also being readied on a war-footing to host the Republic Day parade on January 26, 2022.

The PM is not the focus on Republic Day—it is the President of India and the Armed Forces, and **the Congress party and shameless Leftist journalists are insulting these two institutions of our democracy** by opposing the project, or trying to get it delayed by hook or by crook.

Neither TATA Projects nor Shapoorji Pallonji are Gujarati companies. Both belong to the minority Parsi community, and are amongst the three largest construction companies in India.

The CVP includes residential enclaves for the Vice President and the PM, with the Vice President's residential enclave expected to get completed in end-2022, and the Prime Minister's residential complex expected to get completed in mid-2023. Modi has been criticised for building a 'grand new palace' for himself.

Journalist Alpana Kishore wrote in *Newslaundry* "*Such self-indulgence may be common in dictatorships, but is inappropriate for a Republic. On the other hand, if we are in the Beijing–Moscow– Pyongyang axis where citizens are passive spectators, it is absolutely normal.*"

We estimate that the entire PM's residential complex will cost less than ₹500 crores, including special security measures such as a direct underground tunnel to the new Parliament building. Is this too much for a permanent residence for the chief executive of the world's second largest country and sixth largest economy?

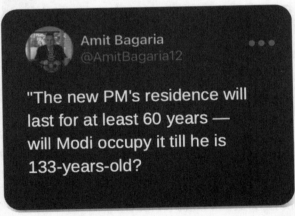

Even if the NDA wins the 2024 general elections and Modi becomes PM again, we are sure he will give up the post soon after September 17, 2025, when he reaches the age of 75, as he has done for all his ministers.

Therefore, at best, Modi will live in the new home for a little over two years. **Besides, the construction of the PM's residential complex is not part of Phase 1.**

Prime Minister Lal Bahadur Shastri chose 10 Janpath as his official residence, though Prime Minister Nehru had lived at Teen Murti Bhawan. Indira Gandhi chose 1 Safdarjung Road. Rajiv Gandhi chose 7 Race Course Road (now 7 Lok Kalyan Marg). This was all OK as they were from the Congress?

> It is OK for Sonia Gandhi to reside in a 1,63,475 sq. feet govt-owned house, larger than the 1,51,845 square feet 7LKM? Rahul lives in a separate 54,085 sq. feet govt-owned house. I don't know why Modi does not throw out Sonia and Rahul from such large houses, and make way for 20–22 new houses for ministers who actually do some work.

Alpana wrote, "*The biggest irony remains that a PM from the humblest of backgrounds should yearn for a house on Rajpath, no less, to endorse his vision of personal greatness and legacy. Would Emmanuel Macron [President of France] demand and, more importantly, get a house on the Champs Elysée? Can even Trump order himself a second home on the Mall?*"

It is surprising a 'senior' journalist like her didn't do research on the subject—or did she know the truth but chose to hide it? The President of France's residence is the 1,20,330 square feet "Elysée Palace" located just 500 meters from the iconic Champs-Élysées. He also has the use of other homes, including the "Fort de Brégançon" off the French Riviera near Marseille and the "La Lanterne", a hunting lodge in Versailles, a 35-minute drive from Élysée Palace.

Should Modi build a beach mansion in Goa and a hunting lodge in Uttarakhand, Ms Alpana Kishore?

Now let us come to Trump, who was POTUS when she wrote the article. POTUS has a second home: a 200–acre country retreat called "Camp David". Even though it's only 103-km from The White House (the official residence), POTUS mostly flies there on three (and sometimes up to five) helicopters, each costing about ₹1650 crore, the rest serving as decoys. The presidential fleet has 35 helicopters.

The Leftist media's favourite, Joe Biden ordered 23 new helicopters for ~₹36,600 crores.

The AMB also call Narendra Modi a fascist, comparing him often with Russian President Vladimir Putin and Turkish President Recep Tayyip Erdoğan. In 2014, Erdoğan built himself a 1,000-room, 31 lakh square feet palace for US$615 million (₹9,620 crore in 2021 prices based on Turkey' inflation). The Indian PM's new residence will be built at less than 6% of that cost.

Coming back to the project components, the CVP will have a Defence Enclave comprising three buildings, with offices of the Ministry of Defence, the Chief of Defence Staff and the three service chiefs, with special security arrangements.

There will be six other buildings to house all the other ministries and departments (apart from defence) of the GOI and their subordinate organisations.

All nine buildings have been labelled as the Central Secretariat in the 2027 Master Plan image.

The Conference Centre will be the largest government conference facility in the world.

There will be total office space for ~53,000 people, and parking for almost 10,000 vehicles in basements. With the retained buildings accommodating another ~17,000 people, there will be ~70,000 physically inter-connected GOI employees. There will be no surface parking. An underground Metro and underground walkways will connect most buildings. Employee efficiency and output will greatly improve due to shorter distances and standardised modern infrastructure with more natural lighting and much improved air quality than in the existing buildings, especially the 'South and North Blocks' designed by Edward Lutyens.

South Block, which currently houses the PMO, the cabinet secretariat, the defence and foreign ministries, and the Office of the NSA, will be converted to a National Museum with the theme 'India up to 1857'. North Block, which currently houses the home and finance Ministries, will be converted to a National Museum with the theme 'India since 1857'.

The GOI spends ₹1000 crore per year as rent and ~₹300 crore on excess security and transport costs due to various ministries and Army/IAF/Navy headquarters not being within walking distance. The investment will be recovered by saving these costs. There will also be some revenue from the museums. And what is the cost vs. benefit of improved efficiency?

The Central Vista zone will be somewhat similar to the area around the "National Mall" in Washington, D.C. (see Pic), which includes the White House, the U.S. Capitol (parliament house), the Supreme Court, several other government buildings, many museums, parks and several monuments. Almost 2.2 crore domestic tourists visited the Mall in 2018—with India's population being ~4.2 times that of the US, imagine the tourism potential of the new Central Vista.

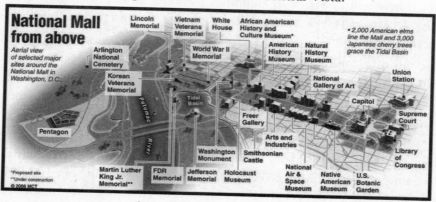

Alpana Kishore also wrote about "secrecy and subterfuge" in the selection of the master planner/architect, *"With the contract going to a Gujarat architecture firm [HCP Design, Planning & Management] known to be particularly close to the PM, whose previous projects had depended for their execution upon the removal of 'obstacles' like due process, impact assessments, public consultation, and well-established global best practices."*

HCP started 41 years before Modi became CM of Gujarat in 2001. They designed the RBI's Ahmedabad Office in 1971, when there was a Congress CM and the Indira Gandhi–appointed S. Jagannathan was the RBI governor. In 1985, they designed the Entrepreneurship Development Institute of India, when Rajiv Gandhi was PM. In 1986, HCP designed the refurbishment of the Eden Gardens cricket stadium in Calcutta, where there was a CPI(M) government. In 1992, they designed the Gujarat High Court when Chimanbhai Patel of Janata Dal was CM. In 1994, HCP designed the CG Road redevelopment project in Ahmedabad, when there was another Congress CM. Should we go on?

In April 2020, after *Hindustan Times* refused to publish an attack against the CVP (which supported Kishore's article) by the so-called historian Ramachandra Guha in his regular weekly columns, Guha quit from *Hindustan Times* and got it published in anti-Modi website *The Wire*. Guha wrote, "*I share her concerns entirely. The PM's own justification is that it was to mark not a personal but a national milestone—the 75th anniversary of Indian independence. This is disingenuous, because past anniversaries had not called for such a spectacular extravaganza. Both the 25th and 50th anniversaries had been suitably marked, by a special session of Parliament. Apparently, what was good enough for Indira Gandhi and IK Gujral wouldn't quite do for Modi.*"

Are special Parliament sessions suitable celebrations of such important milestones? And why does Modi need to copy Indira or Gujral? He's a PM who has done many things differently.

Guha wrote, "*The Modi government's redesign of Delhi brings to mind not so much living communist autocrats as it does some dead African despots. It is the sort of vanity project, designed to perpetuate the ruler's immortality, that Felix Houphouet-Boigny of the Ivory Coast and Jean Bédel-Bokassa of the Central African Republic once inflicted on their own countries.*"

In 1998, Australia built a new Parliament. In 2001, Malaysia built Putrajaya, a new capital city. In 2007, South Korea began construction of its new capital Sejong City, with some ministries relocating from Seoul in 2012. Complete relocation of the capital is expected by 2030. In August 2019, Indonesia announced a new capital. Thailand's new ₹5,400 crore Parliament House opened this month. Are these countries also like Ivory Coast or Central African Republic?

Let's come back to India. Chandra Babu Naidu had started building a
new capital city at Amravati (see Pic) for Andhra Pradesh at an estimated
cost of ₹55,000 crores (more than four times the CVP), before he was
voted out in 2019.

In 2001, Rajasthan completed a new Assembly building. In 2005,
the Congress government built a replica of the old Assembly building
in Bengaluru, which didn't have enough space (same logic doesn't
apply to the new Parliament?). In 2012, Karnataka CM Kumaraswamy
(a Congress partner) built a new Assembly building for almost ₹500
crores (₹833 cr. today) in Belagavi. Why did Karnataka need a second
capital?

In 2010, DMK (another Congress partner) started building a new
Assembly building for ₹1,200 crores (₹2366 cr. today) in Chennai. The
foundation stone was laid by Sonia Gandhi and Dr Manmohan Singh
and over ₹3 crores were spent on a temporary dome. After taking over
as CM in 2011, Jayalalithaa converted the incomplete building to a
hospital-cum-medical college.

In 2013, Mamata Banerjee started a ₹350 crore (₹534 cr.) project
to revamp the Colonial-era Writers' Building. In the meantime, she
spent ₹50 crores on renovating a temporary office on the Howrah
side of the Hooghly river. In 2016, CM Akhilesh Yadav (yet another
Congress partner) inaugurated a ₹602 crore (₹816 cr.) new Secretariat at
Lucknow, UP. In 2019, Naveen Patnaik inaugurated a new Secretariat at
Bhubaneswar, Odisha. Telangana's KC Rao is building new Assembly and
Secretariat buildings for ₹617 crores.

All of these are justified, right Ms Kishore and Mr Guha, because they are all non-BJP governments?

Even during COVID-19, three Congress states announced plans for new buildings. In August 2020, the Chhattisgarh government announced a 5.65 lakh square feet Assembly building, 81.4% the size of the country's new Parliament building.

In the first week of May 2021, at the height of the second wave of COVID-19, the Shiv Sena–NCP–Congress "Maha Vikas Aghadi" government in Maharashtra floated a tender of ₹900 crores for a MLA hostel of ~10 lakh square feet. Not only is this proposed building more expensive than the new Parliament, the contractor (Maharashtra PWD Department) says the cost will shoot up further, with the electrical cost alone estimated at ₹250 crores. The tender cost of ₹9,000/sq.ft. is >1.4x the cost of constructing a 5-star hotel. And no way can the electrical cost be more than ₹40 crores. **We won't be surprised if more than ₹300 crores comes to the coffers of the Shiv Sena–NCP–Congress in the form of kickbacks.**

On June 3, 2021, the Rajasthan Government cleared a ₹266 crore project in record time to build 160 luxurious four-bedroom flats of 3,200 square feet each for MLAs in Jaipur; as well as a ₹60 crore Auditorium in Jodhpur. Building bylaws were flouted for the MLA flats. A 92 feet tall building was allowed as a "special case" against a 50 feet rule. The building will have 1,200 parking spaces, or 7.5 per MLA. Wow!

Architect and conservation consultant AG Krishna Menon wrote in *The Print* on March 8, 2020, that BJP wants to 'erase' colonial heritage. Why should India keep 'colonial' heritage 75 years after Independence? Is the British Raj something for us to cherish? He also inferred that the CVP does not take care of (ecological) conservation. There is no basis for this. The Central Vista will free up ~75 acres for public use. In addition, a 50-acre Biodiversity Arboretum has been planned behind Rashtrapati Bhavan, which will have plants from many different climatic zones of India.

The CVP area currently has 4,642 trees—1,412 shall be retained and 3,230 transplanted to the upcoming 884-acre NTPC Eco Park at Badarpur (See *Times of India* infographic).

NTPC's eco park in Badarpur will be one of the largest manmade parks in the country

AREA **884 acres** | **DEADLINE** **2022**

➤ Park is being built over the fly-ash area of Badarpur Thermal Power Plant, which was shut down last year

➤ Levelling of the area has been done and greening activities will begin soon

➤ Park will be bigger than New York's Central Park spread over 842 acres

FACILITIES TO COME UP

➤ Open safaris in jeeps for visitors as herbivores will be introduced in the park

➤ Yoga centres

➤ Jogging & bicycle tracks

➤ Different sections consisting of lawns, forests and lakes

➤ Observatory mound

➤ Eco-friendly plazas

➤ Sports zones

➤ Various types of fountain displays

➤ Open sitting areas around waterbodies

No tree is being cut and no old Jamun tree from Lutyens' era is being transplanted. About 400 trees already transplanted have a survival rate is over 80%. The overall green cover in the Central Vista will increase, with a net gain of 563 trees. 36,083 trees will be planted in Delhi, including 32,330 trees in the Eco Park.

All buildings will have access to the underground metro with pedestrian subways and will have only underground parking spaces. Plus thousands of daily vehicle trips between currently scattered offices will be reduced.

All this will reduce the carbon footprint from the existing Lutyens Zone and will also reduce pollution.

The Congress and AMB's argument of not enough money being spent on COVID-19 relief measures is completely baseless. The GOI has sanctioned ₹35,000 crores for vaccination. The GOI and the RBI have sanctioned over ₹27.45 lakh crores towards other relief measures.

On May 1, 2021, the GOI released ₹8,873 crores to the State Disaster Relief Fund without waiting for utilisation certificates of the amounts provided to states in the last year. Disaster relief funds of ₹30,000 crores had been given by the GOI to states in the prior year. On May 5, 2021, the RBI (Reserve Bank of India) opened an on-tap liquidity window of ₹50,000 crore with tenors of up to three years at an interest rate of 4% till March 31, 2022, to boost provision of immediate liquidity for ramping up Covid-related healthcare infrastructure and services. All of this out together is 114.75 times our estimated cost for the CVP.

Besides, only ₹1339 crore is being spent on the CVP till August 2022, which is just 0.047% of the money being spent on COVID-19 relief measures by the GOI.

Congress leaders have spent more than an estimated ₹20 crores on foreign travel from the time the pandemic started in India. Couldn't they pay for 16 PSA medical oxygen generation plants instead of this?

Phase-1 of the CVP has created direct and indirect employment for over 25,000 people, which is needed, isn't it? AAP spokesperson Reena Gupta said that the Modi government should pay construction workers ₹5000 per month to stay at home. Wow! Let's create a few lakh more dole-seekers in India.

AAP MLA Mukesh Ahlawat tweeted that the cost of the CVP can pay for 15 AIIMS hospitals. While the actual number would have been 8–9 AIIMS hospitals, should we not compare with the multiple (alleged) scams during the Sonia-rule (2004–2014)? The ₹10.3 lakh crore Bank NPA scam would have paid for 350 AIIMS, the ₹1.856 lakh crore CoalGate scam 63 AIIMS, the ₹1.76 lakh crore 2G scam 60 AIIMS, the ₹70,000 crore CWG scam 24 AIIMS, the ₹61,250 crore Fake Employees scam 21 AIIMS, amongst many others. All the scams put together in the Sonia-Manmohan era would have paid for a minimum of 600 AIIMS hospitals, almost one for every district in India.

During Congress / UPA rule, the office of Lok Sabha Speaker Meira Kumar (a Congressperson nominated for the post by the Congress party) sent a letter in July 2012 to the Ministry of Housing & Urban Affairs, stating that the Speaker has given approval for the construction of a new Parliament building. The letter said that the issue should be given TOP PRIORITY.

This letter stated: "*The Parliament building was constructed in the 1920s ... Over the decades on account of ageing and over use the building has started showing the signs of distress at various places. The present sitting capacity of Lok Sabha and Rajya Sabha is likely to go up after 2026. The seats in Lok Sabha may go up before 2026 also if Women's Reservation Bill provided for augmented strength is passed by the Parliament. In such a scenario it will be necessary to have a new Lok Sabha chamber with larger sitting capacity.*" The letter further stated that instructions should be given to the Central Public Works Dept. to find an area close to the existing Parliament complex and to identify a suitable location for constructing a state-of-the-art new Parliament building.

"*We badly need a parliament building. This one simply isn't functional and is outdated,*" said then Union Minister for Rural Development Jairam Ramesh.

Yet the Congress is attacking Modi for doing the exact same thing. This exposes yet another duplicity of the Congress party.

Do you know why the Congress is opposing not only the Parliament building, but the entire Central Vista Project? There are four main reasons.

The **Sonia government** wanted to build a ~3.75 lakh square feet (area unconfirmed) Parliament building at an estimated cost of ₹600 crores in 2012, or ₹16,000/sq.ft. (**₹26,656/sq.ft.** crores at today's cost).

The **Modi government** is building a 6.94 lakh square feet building @ ₹862 crores, or **₹12,420/sq.ft.** So the Congress has missed a big opportunity, if you get what we mean.

Secondly, many buildings that the GOI currently leases in Central Delhi and which may become useless after the CVP is complete, are **owned by Congress leaders**. An Enquiry Commission should be immediately set up to ascertain how many Congress-leader-owned buildings across India are leased to the GOI and state governments, various departments, PSUs, and other government organisations.

Thirdly, the delimitation exercise due in 2016 will reduce the proportional number of seats in Tamil Nadu and Kerala, where the Congress still has some existence. Therefore, Congress's seat share in the Lok Sabha is likely to go down even more after delimitation.

Fourthly, like we said earlier, the Congress does not want Modi to get the credit for something that will ultimately make all Indians proud. Yes, many of the same people who are criticizing the project now will start praising it in the years to come. Most are known to change their colours and go with the popular flow of the times.

Never again will Central government offices be overcrowded, dirty and stinky. Never again will its employees waste time in commuting. Corruption will reduce because all public meeting rooms are being put in the front part of every ministry building in the CVP with glass walls. And all Indians will be proud of a new capital city (well, almost all!).

PM CARES Fund

Here is how some of the money from the PM CARES Fund has been utilised. We are sure much more has been spent towards fighting the pandemic, but all details will only be available when the Audit reports for FY2020–21 and FY2021–22 come out.

Particulars	₹ Crores
Given to States on 15-Jan 2021	6,309
Ventilators, PPE, N95 Masks	5,022
Vaccination – Phase 1	2,200
1213 nos. PSA Oxygen Plants	1,540
Insurance for 22.14 lakh Health Workers	1,063
Migrant Worker Welfare	1,000
1.5 lakh Oxycare Systems	323
Vaccine Development	100
Hydroxychloroquine Tablets	70
TOTAL	17,627

Unfortunately, the PM did not donate anything to the Mamata Banerjee property purchase account or to her party MP Mohua Mitra's saree purchase account.

Yellow Journalism?

Journalism used to be a vocation. Now it is a business! Information is misused and misreported to create chaos, confusion, and conflict. It is unfortunate that political propaganda has superseded the nation's agenda.

India is probably witnessing its worst crisis since our Independence. It is a health crisis. It is not a crisis India has had any prior experience in dealing with. In fact, the COVID-19 pandemic is a health crisis that no nation in the world has any experience in dealing with.

However, instead of battling this scourge unitedly; some of us Indians, especially some in the media have decided to use it as an opportunity to pander to a sadistic pleasure of spreading fear and leaving the people of India with no hope.

Every Monday, we see leading newspapers and TV channels reporting that cases have fallen in India. Then, on Tuesdays, they raise an alarm saying that the cases are really shooting up. Amit wrote 231 research-based blog posts (www.bagariaamit.com) on COVID-19 between March and November 2020. In more than 25, he wrote that the number of reported cases is low every Sunday in most countries, as testing falls on Saturdays. Further, cases are

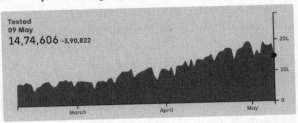

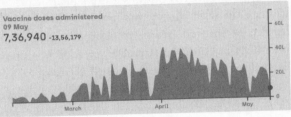

even lower on Mondays as testing on Sundays is the lowest in any given week. Please see these graphs to understand how not only testing, but even the vaccination dips on Sundays. What can Modi do if people do not get tested or vaccinated on Sundays? Should he send 51 ministers to personally visit 31 crore homes to ensure this doesn't happen?

Doesn't the media understand this basic reality for them to keep reporting the same nonsense week after week? Yes, the media is not only full of severely biased journalists, but many journalists also who will write/report anything if they are getting paid for it. In addition, there are unfortunately several with very low IQ.

India's plight during the second wave of the deadly coronavirus was mocked by the Communist Party of China (CPC). An account on Chinese microblogging site Weibo, which was linked to the CCP's Central Political and Legal Affairs Commission, posted a now-deleted photo of China launching a rocket, alongside an image of bodies being cremated in India, with the message: "China lighting a fire, India lighting a fire". An organization linked to CCP resorting to belittling India over the deaths of our people is not shocking because, after reportedly leaking the coronavirus from the Wuhan Lab and putting tens of lakhs of lives in the world at risk due to the COVID-19 pandemic, expecting humanity from people in the Chinese Communist Politburo is like asking Hitler to throw six million (60 lakh) birthday parties for Jews.

The Chinese government mouthpiece **Global Times** accused India of being caught off guard by the COVID-19 pandemic: "*Now, Oxford Economics warned that the brutal coronavirus resurgence in India would raise concerns that Indian economy's nascent recovery will be derailed. When the resurgence of tens of thousands is formed in a poor and populated country like India, the upward trend is going to develop for a couple of weeks if not months.*"

Toeing the Chinese line, Pakistani media also took pot-shots at India. **The Dawn** reported on how India's healthcare system has been struggling to keep up with the second wave of the pandemic. It stated, "Coverage by media showed heart wrenching scenes of patients facing difficulty breathing queuing on stretchers outside hospitals waiting to be treated or let inside hospitals running at full capacity."

An editorial published in the UK's **The Guardian** said: "*The Indian Prime Minister's overconfidence lies behind the country's disastrous Covid-19* *response. The Indian Prime Minister suffers from overconfidence in his own instincts and pooh-poohs expert advice. The buck stirs with him.*" Two months before the 2019 elections, UK's *The Guardian* wrote an editorial with the headline: "*The Guardian view on India's Mr Modi: suppressing inconvenient facts.*" Look at this January 12, 2021, article in *The Guardian* on their own country's National Health Service (NHS).

Subscribe → The **Guardian**

News Opinion Sport Culture Lifestyle

Opinion
This is what an 'overwhelmed NHS' looks like. We must not look away
Christina Pagel

The UK's ***BBC*** reported that cases have surged during India's second wave, driven by a number of factors: health protocols have been lax, with mask mandates sporadically enforced. It further stated, "*India's healthcare system is buckling as a record surge in Covid-19 cases puts pressure on hospital beds and drains oxygen supplies. Families are left pleading for their relatives who are desperately ill, with some patients left untreated for hours.*" *BBC* wrote in December 2018: "*Narendra Modi: Is hardline Hindu politics failing India's PM?*"

The Financial Times in the UK warned that "*Unless the Indian prime minister takes accountability for his role in this crisis more funeral pyres will burn across his nation.*" It also reported that tough questions are being asked of Modi's pandemic management, including public health messages that suggested the virus threat had passed; the failure to heed repeated expert warnings of an imminent second wave; and a botched procurement strategy that has led to an acute shortage of vaccines.

The Economist magazine detailed India's trajectory leading up to the second wave and pinned the blame for the crisis on the Prime Minister and his administration, stating that Modi's slowness to respond to an avalanche of grief had led to the catastrophic second wave. During the 2019 elections, it had written: "*Under Modi, India's ruling party poses a threat to democracy.*"

It is important to note that another January 2021 article in the UK said that England has 62% more patients in hospitals than during the first wave, and the NHS faces the most dangerous situation in living memory, and that hospitals could be overwhelmed within two weeks. "*Some hospitals in England are very oxygen-stressed ... patients will keep arriving in hospitals without enough beds to accommodate them.*" London Mayor Sadiq Khan warned that the city's NHS system was already overwhelmed.

On May 29, the UK had 3.28x cases and 8x deaths per lakh compared with India. **Modi's approval rating was 65% compared to UK PM Boris Johnson's 50%.**

As we have explained earlier, an approval rating for a country's chief executive indicates his/her popularity and therefore the percentage of people who are likely to vote for him/her if elections were held that day.

The French Media too got into the act of questioning India's inability to contain the pandemic. French newspaper *Le Monde* opined that Modi's lack of foresight, arrogance and demagoguery are evidently among the causes of a situation that now seems out of control. On May 29, France had 4.32x cases and 7.15x deaths per lakh compared with India. **French President Emmanuel Macron's approval rating was only 35%.**

The Japan Times opined about the loosening of Modi's grip on India as it struggles under the crippling weight of the collapse of the Indian healthcare system. **That was laughable, as Japanese PM Yoshihide Suga had an approval rating of a pathetic 26%.** In July 2017, *The Japan Times* had said: "*Modi's actions fail to live up to his words: Three years on, it's hard for even the most ardent Indophile to remain optimistic about the nation's future.*"

Ravi Velloor, Associate Editor of *The Straits Times*, Singapore, wrote: "*An unmasked Modi, who addressed campaign rallies in several states, gave the wrong message to the people in letting their guard down. One of the questions from the Indian catastrophe that I have been puzzling over is what happens in Cabinet discussions led by Mr Modi. His minister for health is a qualified doctor and what's more, chairs the WHO's executive board. Two of his Cabinet colleagues are distinguished retirees from the Indian Foreign Service who've spent entire careers focusing on the world outside. The unfolding health disaster is a hybrid of a natural disaster compounded by complacency, misgovernance, and power play.*"

In a report quoting the Morning Consult approval rating tracker which we have also used in earlier chapters and here, ***Al Jazeera*** said: *"Modi, who swept to power in 2014 and was re-elected in 2019 with the biggest majority of any Indian leader in 30 years, has long fostered the image of a powerful Hindu nationalist leader. But India's COVID-19 caseload surged past 25 million this week, exposing a lack of preparation and eroding Modi's support base."*

The Australian newspaper in its article titled 'Modi leads India into viral apocalypse' said, "Arrogance, hyper-nationalism and bureaucratic incompetence have combined to create a crisis of epic proportions, critics say, as India's crowd-loving PM basks while citizens literally suffocate." India's High Commission in Canberra sent this rejoinder to the article.

> **Dear Mr. Dore**
>
> **Re: "Modi leads India into viral apocalypse"**
>
> Our attention has been brought to the above article written by Mr.Philip Sherwell in THE TIMES dated 25 April 2021 and reproduced subsequently in The AUSTRALIAN.
>
> 2.　It is astonishing to see that your respected publication has chosen to reproduce a completely baseless, malicious and slanderous article without bothering to check the facts of the case with any authorities in the Government of India. It appears that the report has been written only with the sole objective of undermining the universally acclaimed approach taken by the Government of India to fight against the deadly global pandemic, at this decisive moment.
>
> 3.　Starting off with the longest and strictest lockdown in the world to the ongoing Covid-19 vaccination drive, the world's largest and fastest to reach 140 million, Indian Government has taken a number of measures to control the pandemic. Massive upgradation in diagnostics (1.7 million tests on 25 April 2021) and treatment facilities undertaken in a record time have saved hundreds of millions of lives and have been praised by the entire global community. Our much acclaimed VACCINE MAITRI initiative to send 66 million vaccines to 80 countries and also to supply medicines and PPEs to 150 countries earlier probably saved hundred of millions more around the world.
>
> 4.　With regard to the recent surge in infections, all possible measures are being taken on a war footing by authorities in India and we are confident that the surge will be contained very soon. Welfare of every citizen of India remains the highest priority for the Government of India. While our scientific community is still looking at possible reasons for the sudden surge in infections, including on the role of infectious new strains that came from outside India, the article has strangely rushed to blame the surge on the restricted election campaign by Hon'ble Prime Minister of India and one religious gathering.
>
> 5.　Coverage of such motivated and malicious reports in your publication only helps in spreading falsehoods and undermining humanity's common fight against the pandemic. Needless to add, it does no good to the reputation of your own publication. I hope you will publish this rejoinder to set the records straight and also refrain from publishing such baseless articles in future.

Australian TV channel ***ABC*** blamed the Indian government for Covid-19 complacency. It stated, *"Not only is the surge far more aggressive* *and deadly than the one India endured last year, but there is a much stronger belief that this catastrophe could have, and should have, been easily avoided. There are three key factors behind what went wrong: government, public behavior and variants."* **Australian PM Scott Morrison's approval rating was 54%.**

The American media went on an overdrive in criticizing the Modi government, though **US President Joe Biden's approval rating was 54%.** It portrayed the Modi government as a failed government in dealing with the COVID-19 pandemic. Their target for ridicule was also one of India's most globally popular cultural religious festivals, the Kumbh Mela, just like the UK's *BBC* attributed the sudden surge of millions of cases in India's second wave to the Mela.

The Washington Post reported that the sudden wave was caused by India relaxing restrictions too soon. *"Tens of thousands of spectators were allowed to fill stadiums for cricket matches; movie theaters were opened; and the government permitted enormous religious gatherings such as the Kumbh Mela, a festival in which millions of Hindus gathered to bathe in the river Ganges."*

The New York Times had an article which said that complacency and government missteps have helped turn India from a seeming success story into one of the world's worst-hit places. India's vaccination rollout was *"late and riddled with setbacks,"* the NYT said. In May 2018, Hartosh Singh Bal wrote in NYT: *"India's Embattled Democracy: Institutions from the judiciary to the media have been corroded during Modi's four years."*

The Wall Street Journal expressed skepticism and quoted researchers: *"With its population of more than 1.3 billion people and skyrocketing infections, India has a higher chance of developing variants, which may take root and spread beyond its borders."*

Time magazine questioned how India was caught unprepared when cases started rising. It went on to criticize India's PM stating, *"The responsibility lies with a strongman regime that has ignored all caution. It lies with the sycophantic cabinet ministers who praised Modi for successfully dealing with Covid-19 in India even as testing slowed down and allowed people to become more complacent about the virus."* It also took a dig at the Indian media *"The government's handling of the pandemic has now made the scale of COVID-19 damage difficult to hide for even the staunchest of its media friends. But it is that media's Pavlovian obeisance to power that helped the build-up of this epic tragedy. A media trained to amplify the ruling party uncritically failed to hold it to account when there was time, and force real action. All that has happened—the collapsing healthcare system, the mountains of corpses, the nationwide hunt for oxygen and the scramble for a piece of earth to give the dead the dignity denied to them in life—is as much on the media as it is on the government."* They forgot to mention how corpses Almost towards the end of the 2019 elections, *Time* had called Modi 'India's Divider-in-Chief'.

Getty Images was selling images of Hindu funeral pyres for ₹7,000 to ₹23,000, depending on the resolution of the pics.

The Post, NYT, WSJ, *Time* and Getty should also have compared their own country's situation during its second wave which lasted from the beginning of October 2020 to the end of April 2021. This was the situation in their largest city, the one and only New York City.

The medical journal **The Lancet** published a report by Anoo Bhuyan from Delhi which says: "*Despite the pandemic and the risk of a major rise in cases, central and state governments also permitted the Hindu festival of Kumbh Mela to go ahead. Millions of Hindus turned up to the festival for prayers and a dip in the river Ganges, which is considered auspicious. Local*

authorities reported nearly 2000 cases of COVID-19 detected among people who had come to participate in the festival."

Well, the actual cases which can be attributed to the Kumbh was probably closer to 25,000, but this translates to 275 per lakh (91 lakh people took part in the Kumbh over 94 days), which is very small compared to 4,666 cases per lakh in its home country, the US, in the 94 days since it's Christmas shopping season began in December 2020.

Many of these articles were written by Indian journalists, who get ₹10,000 to ₹30,000 per article from the foreign media organizations, depending on their experience and popularity.

While one can understand the media in China, Pakistan, the US, the UK, and even Japan to make India look weak and to tarnish its leader's image—as this suits their countries' foreign policy (read Amit's book *USAma—Is USA the World's Largest Terrorist?* to understand this better)—it is disturbing and disappointing that some journalists in India sold their souls to the highest bidders and opted to glaringly focus on the funeral pyres at the crematoriums and deaths across numerous hospitals across India.

Their reportage seemed to toe the line of China.

Between April 19 and 21, 2021, some Indian newspapers and news sites reported that the cremations of COVID-19 victims at special COVID cremation sites in some districts were several times more than the official death counts reported by the concerned states.

The reports named three districts in Modi's home state of Gujarat, and one each in UP (where the chief minister is Yogi Adityanath, probably the third-most hated person by the AMB), MP, and Bihar.

Was it a coincidence that all of these are states ruled by the BJP either directly, or in the case of Bihar, in a coalition? Did such cases not happen in opposition-ruled states? This is nothing but biased reporting. You have already seen in the chapter on states that seven out of 12 states with the maximum underreported deaths are opposition states.

Look at this graphic. The one on the left is from an article in *The Times of India* on May 20, which occupied almost an entire page. The one on the right is what the TOI should have reported.

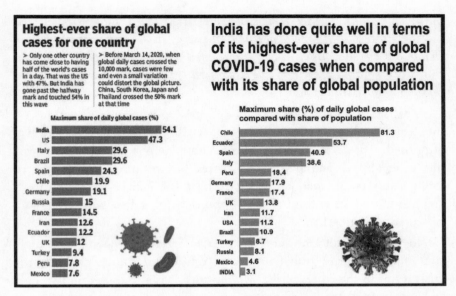

Highest-ever share of global cases for one country

➤ Only one other country has come close to having half of the world's cases in a day. That was the US with 47%. But India has gone past the halfway mark and touched 54% in this wave

➤ Before March 14, 2020, when global daily cases crossed the 10,000 mark, cases were few and even a small variation could distort the global picture. China, South Korea, Japan and Thailand crossed the 50% mark at that time

Maximum share of daily global cases (%)

India	54.1
US	47.3
Italy	29.6
Brazil	29.6
Spain	24.3
Chile	19.9
Germany	19.1
Russia	15
France	14.5
Iran	12.6
Ecuador	12.2
UK	12
Turkey	9.4
Peru	7.8
Mexico	7.6

India has done quite well in terms of its highest-ever share of global COVID-19 cases when compared with its share of global population

Maximum share (%) of daily global cases compared with share of population

Chile	81.3
Ecuador	53.7
Spain	40.9
Italy	38.6
Peru	18.4
Germany	17.9
France	17.4
UK	13.8
Iran	11.7
USA	11.2
Brazil	10.9
Turkey	8.7
Russia	8.1
Mexico	4.6
INDIA	3.1

On April 28, the TOI carried an anti-Modi propaganda advertisement disguised as an article by some Dr Devlina Chakravarty with the headline 'We are witnessing a catastrophe, Show us the way'. The same article by the same writer, verbatim, was published by the online rag The Wire three days before it was printed in TOI. After the TOI was exposed, the article was quickly removed from its website.

In *The Atlantic*, Vidya Krishan wrote that while it would be too easy to lay blame for this crisis entirely at the feet of Modi and his BJP, much can be attributed to his government. After the virus landed on India's shores, he imposed a brutal shutdown—one that largely hurt the poorest and most vulnerable—without consulting the nation's top scientists yet did not use the time to build the country's healthcare infrastructure. HUH? How do you build the country's healthcare infrastructure—which Congress-led or governments that depended on the Congress did not do for 57.3 years—in just a few months? If Ms Krishnan knows how to do it, she doesn't just deserve to be India's health minister, we would vote for her to become the next PM!

Not far behind was Hinduphobic journalist **Rana Ayyub**, who stated on social media, "*Is there a single newspaper in India that will publish the names of those we lost to Covid on the front page? Is there a single newspaper in the country that will ask for Modi's resignation and ask accountability of* *the Prime Minister?'* In a *Time* magazine article titled 'How Modi Failed Us' she wrote: *"If the apocalypse had an image, it would be the hospitals of India … Why was India caught unprepared as the second wave ravaged a cross-section of Indian society? The responsibility lies with a strongman regime that has ignored all caution."*

This same Rana Ayyub was forced to stop accepting donations on the crowdfunding platform Ketto for a COVID-relief effort she was 'supposedly' undertaking, due to concerns about violating FCRA laws. **She allegedly duped people of crores** but returned the money to foreign donors. She had earlier raised over ₹68 lakhs and an unknown amount in two other fundraisers, supposedly for 'relief' work in Assam, Bihar, and Maharashtra.

Journalist Rohit Chopra wrote in **The Scroll** that having seemingly contained the virus, Indians got too complacent too quickly. Yet the crisis is not in the lapses of the two months. It is also rooted in two ugly and intertwined truths. The first is the style of paranoid authoritarian governance practiced and perfected over the last seven years by Modi and his team that has become an effective reason of state in India. *"The second is a malaise endemic to Indian society, whose very worst impulses of indifference to the plight of others are embodied in the figure of Modi and his followers."*

Reuters reporters in India filed stories from hospitals and crematoriums. Some headlines of the stories run by the global newswire agency said, 'COVID patients die on trolleys outside Delhi hospital'. Another headline with heart wrenching photos from Delhi's crematoriums read, 'Mass cremations begin as India's capital faces deluge of COVID-19 deaths'.

On January 19, 2021, Nitin Pai wrote in **The Print**: *"Last August, I estimated that Covid-19 will end its epidemic phase in India by January 2021. It appears that this prediction was not too far off the mark."* Just three months later, on April 22, he wrote" *"Modi govt had a year to prepare for 2nd Covid wave. Now, patients don't have oxygen to breathe."*

The Congress/Gandhi-family-owned **National Herald** carried a piece by Gyan Pathak stating, *"Prime Minister Modi's leadership is held responsible all over the world and is being criticized for driving India into such a miserable condition. Real data was allegedly suppressed by incorrect* *counting of infections and deaths on the one hand and testing efforts were drastically reduced after the peak of mid-September 2020, resulting in steep fall in detection of new cases. On the basis of this false data, PM went on harping on winning corona battle during the first wave. It misled people to behave as if they were out of danger, crowding market or public places and gathering in large numbers is social, religious, or political events."*

The most demeaning piece was an attack on Modi, Home Minister Amit Shah, and UP CM Yogi Adityanath (who is as much hated by the Leftist media as Modi is, if not more) written by Ruchir Joshi in *The Telegraph* (India). This 39-year-old newspaper is bought by ~0.025% of India's population, and over 70% of its readership is in West Bengal, which has elected you-know-who for the third time, after electing Communists seven times. Even Savio's 11-year-old *GoaChronicle* has a higher readership.

The writer calls the PM incompetent and a "fungus". Mr Joshi may have a lower IQ than even Rahul Gandhi, who is perhaps his hero. In August 2019, several high-profile Congress leaders had disapproved of Rahul Gandhi's all-out attack on Modi. Jairam Ramesh said: *"PM Modi's governance model is not a complete negative story and not recognising his work and demonising him all the time is not going to help. It is time we recognise Modi's work and what he did between 2014 and 2019 due to which he was voted back to power by over 30% of the electorate... unless we realise he is doing things which people recognise and which have not been done in the past, we are not going to be able to confront this guy."* Dr Abhishek Manu Singhvi said: *"Always said demonising Modi wrong. Acts are always good, bad & indifferent—they must be judged issue wise and not person wise. Certainly, Ujjwala scheme is only one amongst other good deeds."* Shashi Tharoor tweeted: *"I have argued for six years now that @ narendramodi should be praised whenever he says or does the right thing, which would add credibility to our criticisms whenever he errs."*

Joshi accuses the PM of not having integrity and of criminal law-bending and says that corruption has been rocketed to another dimension under him (now, now Mr Joshi, even most people in the Congress don't subscribe to this theory). He also indirectly accuses the Supreme Court by putting 'judgement' in inverted commas relating to the Ayodhya Ram Mandir.

And what is completely not acceptable is this sadist leftist mocking the Indian Air Force by saying that they bombed a clump of trees in Balakot, Pakistan. Perhaps Joshi should stick to writing erotic books, instead of this kind of rubbish.

These are just a few examples amongst thousands (yes, thousands) of other anti-Modi (and some directly or indirectly anti-India) articles.

In most editorial and opinion pieces, Modi and his government have been blamed for the second wave of the COVID-19 pandemic. Both Modi and Shah have been painted as the primary architects of this health crisis, that could have 'supposedly' been avoided. Citing decisions to go ahead with the Kumbh Mela and holding election rallies where COVID protocols were not followed were the two of the main reasons that the Indian and global media questioned Modi, coupling with their opinion that Modi's arrogance, his supporters' hyper nationalism and his government's officials' bureaucratic incompetence as the underlying failure of India to predict the second wave and be prepared.

We have already stated in the "Notes by the Authors" at the beginning of the book that the Kumbh Mela should not have been held. But we have also questioned why other religious congregations and the farmers' protests—which also did not follow safety protocols—were not highlighted. It is because most media persons, at least in India, are afraid to speak up against any wrongdoings of Muslims. During the month of Ramzan, cases rose sharply in all states with over 20% Muslim population.

There is no doubt that India is going through tough times which makes journalism a difficult ball game. COVID-19 has changed our lives; we are seeing suffering and pain in most places in India. The health crisis has not only engulfed India but most countries in the world. It has touched the entire human race.

Some journalists may have experienced covering a war, as every journalist in a war region knows that there are rules to reporting on war, this too is a war against a pandemic, India and the world has not seen before. While it is easy to use stories to spread fear in the guise of journalistic liberties in a democratic nation, spreading lies to create a fear psychosis among panicked people is wrong.

'Besides COVID-19, India is also fighting with vulture journalists, who are spreading more panic and despair than pandemic', a headline said in *The Australia Today*, with this pic.

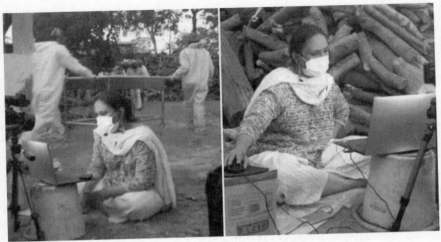

This former TV anchor milked her way till the cows came home in reporting the Kargil War and the 26/11 Mumbai attacks. In the US (the world's oldest democracy), she would have been imprisoned for several years under their Patriot Act and other national security laws, with no chance of a judicial appeal. But in India we allow such shameless people to get away. Why couldn't our intolerant fascist-led government have tried her under UAPA or any other suitable Indian law?

No wonder that in a LinkedIn poll of 1,573 people, as many as 83.73% said that they don't trust the mainstream media.

As Prime Minister Narendra Modi rightly put it: *"This crisis has engulfed the entire human race."*

Yet most writers in the Indian media prefer to focus on the misery, instead of the success stories of ordinary people who have done extraordinary work by going out of their way to address the pandemic at their local levels.

Help Pours In

Over 40 countries helped India during our crisis. If this was not (partly) a result of Modi's overall pre-COVID diplomacy (109 visits to 60 countries, for which he was mocked by the Congress and the rest of the AMB) and his COVID-diplomacy then what were the reasons these countries poured out in support of India? Not only did India send vaccines to 93 countries, but Modi also removed the ban on exports of hydroxychloroquine in April 2020 when President Donald Trump asked for it and eased the ban on exports of Nitrile/NBR gloves in October 2020 in the interest of protecting frontline healthcare workers around the world. Did so many countries support Brazil when they were reporting the world's second-highest numbers? Or the UK, Turkey, or France when numbers shot up there? The answer is no!

The countries that sent us medical oxygen supplies, oxygen concentrators, ventilators, Remdesivir, Tocilizumab and other drugs, masks, PPE kits, and other medical supplies, include Australia, Austria, Bangladesh, Belgium, Bhutan, Canada, China (yes, even China, though they didn't give anything free, except the Coronavirus itself!), Czechia, France, Germany, Hong Kong, Indonesia, Ireland, Kuwait, Luxembourg, Mauritius, New Zealand, Pakistan (yes!), Portugal, Qatar, Romania, Russia, Saudi Arabia, Singapore, Sweden, Thailand, the UAE, and the UK. Let us not forget that Modi has struck personal rapports with the leaders of at least 14 of these countries.

Among the items received by India between April 15 and May 15 alone were 19 oxygen generation plants, 11,058 oxygen concentrators, 13,496 oxygen cylinders, 7,365 ventilators, ~5.3 lakh Remdesivir vials, and over 25,000 rapid antigen test kits.

We are not saying that this was the only reason, but it must have surely played a part. Never before in India's history have so many foreign countries helped us within days of the advent of a crisis. But then, Congress governments till 1984 did not even befriend the West. The only government that did was the first opposition government led by Morarji Desai between March 1977 and July 1979.

Even foreign companies and individuals pitched in. These included Accenture, Amazon, Apple, Boeing, Capgemini (₹50 crore), Deloitte, Facebook (₹75 crore), Google (₹135 crore), IBM, JP Morgan, Lockheed Martin, MasterCard Microsoft, Salesforce, and Walmart. Do not forget that Modi has had one-on-one meetings with the CEOs of most of these companies.

Canadian–Russian software programmer Vitalik Buterin, a cofounder of the cryptocurrency Ethereum, donated $1.14 billion (~₹8440 crores), a bulk of which was in a meme coin called Shiba Inu, to the India COVID-19 Relief Fund set up by and run by Indian crypto entrepreneur Sandeep Nailwal. This is the single largest donation by any person or organization to date. Nailwal explained that the Fund converts crypto into hard currency through an entity in the UAE.

Remdesivir manufacturer Gilead Sciences of the US has pledged to donate 300,000 vials of the drug free of cost to India. The market price of this in the US is $156 million (₹1170 crores).

Indian corporate groups/trusts/organizations and individuals that contributed money, materials and/or resources of over ₹2000 crores (₹20 billion) included Adani and Ambani (the two who have been continuously mocked by the Congress and the AMB), the Tata Group, and the Azim Premji Foundation. In March 2014, Arvind Kejriwal had called Narendra Modi a "property dealer for corporates like Ambani, Adani, and Tatas." Well, the properties are yielding good rental returns, aren't they, Mr Kejriwal? This same man on April 25, 2021, asked the same three corporate groups to help Delhi with the COVID crisis.

The bracket between ₹50-200 crores (₹500 million–2 billion) includes ITC, Hindustan Unilever, Vedanta, Hero, Bajaj, L&T, JSW, Kotak, P&G, Mankind Pharma, ArcelorMittal, Airtel, Infosys, HSBC, Torrent Pharma, cricket body BCCI, Shirdi Temple, actor Akshay Kumar, and former cricketer Sachin Tendulkar. The bracket above ₹20 crores included Mahindra Group, TVS Group, Asian Paints, Patanjali, PayTM, PepsiCo, Ola, CRED, and Zomato. Many public sector (government–

owned) companies have also contributed large amounts in money or materials.

Hotel chains like Taj Group (Indian Hotels), ITC, Trident (Oberoi), Lemon Tree, Sarovar and Oyo offered hundreds of their rooms to hospitals to manage their patient overflow, at deep discounts.

Tamil superstar Rajinikanth, as well as cricketers Virat Kohli and Suresh Raina, also donated large amounts. Telugu actors Prabhas (₹4 cr.), Pawan Kalyan (₹2 cr.), Allu Arjun (₹1.25 cr.), Chiranjeevi (₹1 cr.), Mahesh Babu (₹1 cr.), Junior NTR (₹75 lakhs), and Ram Charan (₹70 lakhs), gave big amounts. Comedian Kapil Sharma gave more than ₹50 lakhs.

Bollywood personalities such as Lata Mangeshkar, Shah Rukh Khan, Salman Khan, Anushka Sharma, Alia Bhatt, Karan Johar, Anupam Kher, Katrina Kaif, Hrithik Roshan, Saif Ali Khan, Kareena Kapoor Khan, Deepika Padukone and Ranveer Singh, Priyanka Chopra, Sonam Kapoor, Rajkumar Rao, Vicky Kaushal, Nana Patekar, Kartik Aaryan, Diljit Dosanjh, rapper Badshah, Varun Dhawan, Shilpa Shetty, Kriti Sanon, Bhumi Pednekar, Ayushman Khurrana, Kartik Aaryan, Randeep Hooda, Sunny Deol, Hema Malini, producer Bhushan Kumar, and some others, had donated to the PM-CARES Fund and other relief measures in 2020. We may have missed out on several more.

But nowhere did we read about contributions from the Modi-haters in Bollywood such as Aamir Khan, Shabana Azmi, Javed Akhtar, Farhan Akhtar, Mahesh Bhatt or his daughter Pooja Bhatt, Tapsee Pannu, Swara Bhaskar, Richa Chada, Nandita Das, Sayani Gupta, Anurag Kashyap, Vishal Bharadwaj, Mohd Zeeshan Ayyub, Twinkle Khanna, Dia Mirza, Naseeruddin Shah, Parineeti Chopra, Huma Qureshi, Konkona Sen Sharma, Riteish Deshmukh, Renuka Shahane, Armaan Malik, or their ilk. They may be anti-Modi, but this is a national crisis—and what is their contribution? Remember this the next time you decide to watch a movie!

A Chinese Bioweapon?

The Coronavirus is not a freak of nature or God's punishment to sinning humankind or anything of that sort. It is a man-made weapon of biowarfare. It originated in Wuhan, China, where the Wuhan Institute of Virology (WIV) was experimenting in dangerous sciences. Whether the new strain of Coronavirus (the SARS-CoV-2 that caused the COVID-19 disease) was deliberately or accidentally leaked from the WIV lab is a matter of investigation.

China knew about the human-to-human transmission of COVID-19, yet it hid the truth from the world. WHO Director General **Dr Tedros Adhanom Ghebreyesus** is widely considered to be a puppet of **Chinese President Xi Jinping**, and played his role quite well to cover up on behalf of China. He even quoted the Chinese authorities' claim that there is no clear evidence of human-to-human transmission of COVID-19.

It was not the first time China covered up an epidemic. It did a cover-up during the SARS epidemic too.

One proof that WHO is a puppet of China is that WHO has not yet approved BB's Indian-developed and made Covaxin vaccine, despite over two crore jabs having been successfully given to people, while it has approved China's Sinopharm vaccine despite several concerns, including: (1) Chinese vaccine expert Dr Tao Lina claimed that it is "extremely unsafe" and has 73 side effects [however, as soon as his post went viral on Chinese social media platform Weibo, the vaccine expert apologised to the nation for his "imprudent" comments and deleted his comments]; (2) Brazil questioned its efficacy after data showed that the Sinopharm vaccine was only 50.4% effective; (3) The UAE and Bahrain are offering a third jab due to efficacy doubts; (4) There has been outrage in the Philippines, Singapore and Malaysia about the Chinese vaccine; and (5)

There was 60% Positivity Rate in Maldives and Seychelles in people who got vaccinated with it.

The China Virus—as so aptly stated by President Donald Trump in mid-May 2020—was then already responsible for over 49.25 lakh cases and over 3.26 lakh deaths globally. A year later, the **cases have gone up 35.5 times to 17.5 crore (almost 2.1% of world population), and deaths 11.4 times to 37.16 lakh**.

The director of the Center for Emerging Infectious Diseases at WIV, **Dr Shi Zhengli**, spoke of this strain of the virus in 2007. Scientist Dr Li Meng Yan, who escaped from China and is now in the US, has revealed the truth about experiments at the WIV lab. In a research paper she co-authored with three other scientists, she stated, "*Unusual features of SARS-CoV-2 suggest sophisticated lab modification rather than natural evolution and delineation of its probable synthetic route.*" In a follow-up research report in October 2020, Dr Yan and other scientists stated, "*Coronavirus is an unrestricted bioweapon.*"

Scientists and doctors from the WIV lab who had initially said that the virus had leaked out from the lab were told to keep quiet. Among them was Dr Li Wenliang. The eight were hauled up by police for "spreading rumours" and forced to sign statements withdrawing their claims. Dr Li died in February 2020 from COVID-19. Media reports also suggest that Chinese labs studying the novel Coronavirus in late-December 2019 and early-January 2020 received orders to destroy their samples.

WHO in its investigative report "Origins of SARS-CoV-2" states that the seafood market in Wuhan City was the source of this Coronavirus outbreak or played a significant role in the initial amplification of the outbreak. Dr Tedros said, "*The team has confirmed that there was widespread contamination with SARS-CoV-2 in the Huanan market in Wuhan but could not determine the source of this contamination.*" Interestingly, in a research paper brought out in February 2020, two researchers at the South China University of Technology had a different opinion to the theory floated by the Chinese Government and WHO on the Huanan seafood market.

According to these Chinese researchers, "*The bats carrying CoV ZC45 were originally found in Yunnan or Zhejiang province, both more than 900-km away from the seafood market. Bats are normally found to live in caves and trees. But the seafood market is in a densely populated district of Wuhan, a city of over 15 million people. The probability was very low for the bats to fly to the market. According to municipal reports and the testimonies of 59 people, the bat was never a food source in the city, and no bat was traded in the market ... We screened the area around the seafood market and identified two labs conducting research on bat coronavirus. Within 280 meters from the market, there was the Wuhan Center for Disease Control & Prevention (WHCDC). WHCDC hosted animals in labs for research purposes, one of which was specialized in pathogens collection and identification. In one of their studies, 155 bats ... were captured in Hubei province, and the other 450 bats were captured in Zhejiang province. The expert in the collection was ... broadcasted for collecting viruses on nationwide newspapers and websites in 2017 and 2019. He described that he was once attacked by bats ... so he quarantined himself for 14 days. Surgery was performed on the caged animals and the tissue samples were collected for DNA and RNA extraction and sequencing. The tissue samples and contaminated trashes were sources of pathogens. They were only 280 meters from the seafood market. The WHCDC was also adjacent to the Union Hospital where the first group of doctors was infected during this epidemic. It is plausible that the virus leaked and contaminated the initial patients, though solid proofs are needed in a future study. The second lab was 12-km from the seafood market and belonged to WIV. This lab reported that the Chinese horseshoe bats were natural reservoirs for the SARS-CoV which caused the 2002-2003 pandemic. The principal investigator [Dr Zhengli] participated in a project which generated a chimeric virus using the SARS-CoV reverse genetics system and reported the potential for human emergence. Direct speculation was that SARS-CoV or its derivative might leak from the lab. In summary ... the killer coronavirus probably originated from a lab in Wuhan."*

The Chinese government censored the research paper of the Chinese researchers Botao Xiao and Lei Xiao. In fact, it has disappeared from the international scholarly data base Research Gate, not the first such incident for texts from China.

Dr Stephen Carl Quay is the founder of Atossa Therapeutics Inc., an American biopharma company developing therapeutics and delivery methods for breast cancer and COVID-19 therapeutics. He holds 87 patents, has more than 360 published articles on medicine and has been cited over 10,000 times, placing him in the **top 1% of scientists worldwide**. Dr Quay's research report revealed, *"Line 2 of the Wuhan*

Metro services the PLA Hospital with the first COVID-19 cluster of patients, the hospitals where patients first went in December 2019 and early January 2020 and is the likely conduit for human-to-human spread throughout Wuhan, China, and the world. The Hunan Seafood Market, WIV, and the Wuhan CDC, all locations suggested to be the possible source of SARS-CoV-2, are also all serviced by Line 2 of the Metro, suggesting this public transit line should become the focus for further investigations into the origin of this pandemic. Line 2 connects to all eight other lines of the Wuhan Metro System facilitating rapid spread in Wuhan and Hubei Province, and also services both the high-speed rail station (Hankou Railway Station), facilitating rapid spread throughout China, and the Wuhan International Airport, facilitating rapid spread throughout Asia, Europe, and to the US."

The first-three cases in India were people who had travelled to Wuhan and returned to Kerala on January 30, 2020.

The real problem that led to the spread of the virus was the delay in categorizing COVID-19 as a pandemic, which happened on March 11, 2020, even though it was declared as a Public Health Emergency of International Concern (PHEIC) by WHO on January 30, 2020. Dr Tedros stated, "We have made the assessment that COVID-19 can be categorized as a pandemic. Pandemic is not a word to use lightly or carelessly. It is a word that, if misused, can cause unreasonable fear, or unjustified acceptance that the fight is over, leading to unnecessary suffering and death." When COVID-19 was categorized as a 'Pandemic' on March 11, there were over 1.4 lakh cases in 174 countries.

Even during the '2009 Swine Flu, Dr Margaret Chan, then Director-General of the WHO declared it as a PHEIC on April 25, 2009, and then on June 11, 2009, categorized it as a 'Pandemic' when there were 30,000 cases in 74 countries. Again, after nearly six weeks. It is baffling that WHO categorized a pandemic in both cases six-weeks later but does not consider a Pandemic as an alert-level used under WHO's emergency response framework. It was only when COVID-19 was categorized as a pandemic that 95 countries around the world initiated a partial or full-lockdown, not when WHO declared COVID-19 as a PHEIC.

Most world leaders, scientists, and doctors now believe that President Jinping has put the lives of crores of people at risk to follow his lofty dreams of global dominance. Which leader sacrifices lakhs of his own people to wage a war against humanity? Finding the origin of Coronavirus should involve an independent audit of the WIV labs and the labs of their close collaborators. Such an investigation should have taken place long ago.

China has reported only 4,636 deaths due to Covid19. Given its population, the figure is likely to be 140 times that number, or ~6.5 lakh. It has reported a sum total of only four deaths (yes, four) in the last 14 months.

The SARS-CoV-2 virus meets the criteria of a bioweapon described by Dr Ruifu Yang of the Beijing Institute of Microbiology and Epidemiology, who is funded by the US government's "**NIH**" (National Institutes of Health) and NSF (National Science Foundation). He is part of China's Academy of Military Medical Sciences, and its Bioterrorism Response Group. In 2005, Dr Yang specified the criteria for a pathogen to qualify as a bioweapon:

1. It is significantly virulent and can cause a large-scale casualty.

2. It is highly contagious and transmits easily, often through respiratory routes in the form of aerosols. The most dangerous scenario is that it allows human-to-human transmission.

3. It is relatively resistant to environmental changes, can sustain transportation, and is capable of supporting the targeted release.

All these criteria have been met by SARS-CoV-2. Its high rate of asymptomatic transmission makes the process of trying to control the virus extremely challenging. Its range and destructive power is unprecedented. SARS-CoV-2 not only meets but also surpasses the standards of a traditional bioweapon. Therefore, it should be defined as an Unrestricted Bioweapon.

The Sun newspaper in the UK, quoting reports of *The Australian* newspaper, said that "bombshell" documents obtained by the US State Department (their foreign ministry) show Chinese People's Liberation Army (PLA) commanders making a sinister prediction that the next World War would be fought with bioweapons. A Chinese military document of 2015 entitled "The Unnatural Origin of SARS and New Species of Man-Made Viruses as Genetic Bioweapons" reveals the Chinese military's plans with regards to bioweapons. The PLA's bioweapon textbook by General Dezhong Xu, points out two significant dimensions of the biological war. First, the ability to freeze-dry micro-organisms has made it possible to store biological agents and aerosolize them during attacks. Second, a bioweapon attack could cause the "enemy's medical system to collapse". The authenticity of the documents has been verified by experts. Digital forensics specialist Robert Potter stated that it has been located on the Chinese internet.

In an interview with the TV channel *India Today*, Dr Li Meng Yan asserted that "*this document is the 'smoking gun' that can prove China has a long-term program of non-traditional bio-weapons and plans to use it to conquer the whole world.*" She also said that she had provided "enough solid scientific evidence together with intelligence evidence" which China can't deny. She had been continuously stating since her arrival in the US that the Coronavirus was made in the Wuhan lab.

American human rights lawyer, Dr. Francis Boyle, professor of international law at the University of Illinois, who drafted the Biological Weapons Anti-Terrorism Act of 1989, had earlier given a detailed statement that the 2019 Coronavirus is a Chinese 'offensive biological warfare weapon'.

If this was a war in which China unleashed its army against any other army in the world, it could be excused, as soldiers are trained to fight wars for their nation, and some will die. But that would be the death of war heroes. Some innocents would also die but they would know which enemy their army is fighting. But Jinping has unleashed a bio-war on the world. He has dragged innocent people who have nothing to do with the geopolitical games played by ambitious global political or military leaders. He has let loose an enemy that cannot be seen. Sixteen months later, the death-toll keeps piling up.

People lived their lives with hope and aspirations, now they are depressed and afraid of life. This Chinese virus has taken away a major necessity of human interaction—touch. It has made touch seem to be an act of violation and probably death. We might live the next few years wearing masks and gloves. Yes, the Chinese virus has changed the world permanently, even though we will defeat it. The transmissibility, morbidity, and mortality of SARS-CoV-2 resulted in panic in the global community, disruption of social orders, and decimation of the world's economy.

Prominent virologists have said that accidental escape from the lab, while not being entirely ruled out, was unlikely, and that genetic evidence suggests that the SARS-CoV-2 genome is a product of genetic manipulation. China has the expertise for the 'convenient' creation of this novel Coronavirus.

The backbone/template virus (ZC45/ZXC21) is owned by Chinese military research labs. The genome sequence is likely to have undergone genetic engineering, through which the virus has gained the ability to target humans with enhanced virulence and contamination. The characteristics and pathogenic effects of SARS-CoV-2 are unprecedented. The virus is highly transmissible, onset-hidden, targets multiple organs, is associated with various symptoms and complications, and is lethal.

Scientific evidence and records indicate that the COVID-19 pandemic is not a result of an accidental release of a gain-of-function product but a planned attack using an Unrestricted Bioweapon. Infected people are being used, without their knowledge, as transmitters of the disease. The first victims of the bioterrorism attack were Chinese people, especially in Wuhan. Initially, the hidden spread in Wuhan could have also served another purpose: the final verification of the bioweapon's functionality, especially the human-to-human transmission efficiency. On the success of this last step, targeted release of the pathogen might have been enabled.

Xi Jinping must be tied as a 'war criminal' along with every other Chinese or non-Chinese person who were accomplices in this dastardly attack on humanity.

Let us also look at the role of some Americans in China's bio-war against the world.

On February 19, 2020, a group of virologists and others wrote in *The Lancet*, "*We stand together to strongly condemn conspiracy theories suggesting that COVID-19 does not have a natural origin. [Scientists] overwhelmingly conclude that this coronavirus originated in wildlife.*" They wrote this when it was far too soon for anyone to be sure what had happened. The signatories of the Lancet letter were behaving as poor scientists. They were assuring the public of facts they could not know for sure were true. It later turned out that *The Lancet* letter had been organized and drafted by **Peter Daszak**, president of the EcoHealth Alliance of New York. Daszak's organization funded coronavirus research at WIV. If the virus had indeed escaped from the research he had funded, Daszak would be potentially culpable. This acute conflict of interest was not declared to readers. On the contrary, the letter concluded, "*We declare no competing interests.*"

In a publication of the chimeric virus SHC015-MA15 in 2015, the fact of Dr Zhengli being funded by "**NIAID**" (National Institute of Allergy and Infectious Diseases, part of the NIH) was initially left out. It was reinstated in 2016 in a corrigendum, perhaps after a meeting in January 2016 to reinstate NIH funding for '**gain-of-function**' research on viruses. This was very unusual scientific behaviour. Gain-of-function refers to the serial passaging of microorganisms to increase their transmissibility, virulence, immunogenicity, and host tropism by applying selective pressure to a culture.

Dr Anthony Fauci heads NIAID since 1984. He was a member of the White House Coronavirus Task Force formed by President Trump in January 2020. On December 3, 2020, President-elect Biden asked Dr Fauci to also become chief medical advisor to POTUS. Dr Fauci has been the most public face of any government in the world, in speaking about COVID-19.

In a report titled 'The Fauci/COVID-19 Dossier', international leader in intellectual-property-based financial risk Dr David E Martin reveals his dossier is indicative of the numerous criminal violations that may be associated with Covid19 terrorism.

An NIH grant (like a scholarship given to individuals, a grant is a financial allowance given to organisations) was issued to gain-of-function specialist **Dr Ralph Baric** at UNC (University of North Carolina,

Chapel Hill, USA, officially affiliated with Dr Fauci's NIAID) to work on synthetically altering the Coronaviridae (the coronavirus family of viruses) for general research, pathogenic enhancement, detection, manipulation, and potential therapeutic interventions targeting the same. As early as May 2000, Dr Baric and UNC sought to patent critical sections of the coronavirus family for commercial benefit.

In April 2002, before the first SARS outbreak in Asia, Dr Baric and two others filed an application for U.S. Patent 7,279,372 for a method of producing a recombinant Coronavirus. They sought to patent a means of producing, "an infectious, replication-defective, Coronavirus." This work was also supported by NIH grants. Thus, the "**HHS**" (the U.S. Department of Health and Human Services is the US's health ministry) was involved in the funding of amplifying the infectious nature of Coronavirus between 1999 and 2002, before SARS was ever detected in humans.

In April 2003, the "**CDC**" (the Centers for Disease Control and Prevention is a national public health agency of the US) sought to patent the SARS Coronavirus isolated from humans that had transferred to humans during the 2002-2003 SARS outbreak in Asia. Their application, updated in 2007, ultimately issued as U.S. Patent 7,220,852, constrained anyone not licensed by their patent from manipulating SARS CoV, developing tests/kits to measure SARS Coronavirus in humans, or working with their patented virus for therapeutic use. Work associated with this virus by their select collaborators included considerable amounts of chimeric engineering, gain-of-function studies, viral characterisation, detection, treatment (including vaccination), and weaponization inquiries. With Baric's and CDC's patents, no research in the US could be conducted without permission or infringement.

Dr Baric was not only the recipient of millions of dollars of US research grants from several government agencies but also sat on the WHO's International Committee on Taxonomy of Viruses and the Coronaviridae Study Group. In this capacity, he was not only responsible for determining "novelty" of clades of virus species, but also directly benefitted from determining declarations of novelty in the form of new research funding authorisations and associated patenting and commercial collaboration. Together with CDC, NIAID, WHO, and pharma/biotech companies (including J&J, Sanofi, Moderna, Ridgeback, Gilead, Sherlock

Biosciences, and others who produce test kits, vaccines or treatment drugs for Covid19), a powerful group constituted "interlocking directorates" under U.S. anti-trust laws.

Donald Trump stood up to China and held China accountable for the pandemic. China used its stealth propaganda machinery to create panic and lack of trust in the Trump administration, which resulted in Trump losing the November 2020 presidential election. President Joe Biden wants 'competition' and not 'conflict' with China. China has the US where it wants it—barking but not biting.

China is adopting a similar strategy in India. It is using its unlimited funds and its huge propaganda machinery within India and internationally to discredit Narendra Modi and the Indian government. The Chinese propaganda machinery, with the help of its supporters within India (the AMB), is creating chaos and confusion in the minds of the people.

While India battles COVID-19, China may also spark communal tensions in India in the weeks or months ahead. It may also create tensions along the border. China will keep the Indian government busy and heighten the negative propaganda.

China will work for a change of regime in India too, just like it did in the US. It wants a regime in India that is more favourable to its global agenda.

It has already forged an alliance with the Congress. The Nehru-Gandhi-family run Rajiv Gandhi Foundation (RGF) received donations of $300,000 in 2005-06 (almost ₹4.2 crores in current value) from the Communist Party of China (CPC). The Rajiv Gandhi Institute of Contemporary Studies, a part of RGF, has some kind of partnership with the China Association for International Friendly Contact, an organisation of China's Central Military Commission, which is under scrutiny by the US's FBI and other global agencies which suspect it could be a spy agency for China's PLA. Since Modi became PM seven years ago, Congress has been toeing the line of China. On 7 August 2008 Rahul Gandhi and Wang Jiarui, director of the International Liaison Department (ILD) of the Communist Party of China (CPC) signed a Memorandum of Understanding in the presence of Sonia Gandhi and Xi Jinping, who was then the Vice President of China. The ILD is not only a Chinese foreign policy influencer but is also suspected to be a covert Chinese spy agency.

In fact, a few leaders in the BJP have also been kind in their words on China, not confrontational. **Yes, there are many corrupt people in the BJP who want to oust the incorruptible Modi**.

In its retaliation, India will be forced to toe the diplomatic line that a democratic nation does. China has no obligation or scruples. It will work towards humiliating India at every opportunity. Its strategy will be multi-pronged. It will attack India socially and economically.

This Twitter poll conducted by senior journalist Abhijit Majumder shows that 82% Indians believed (as of May 5) that China unleashed COVID-19 deliberately.

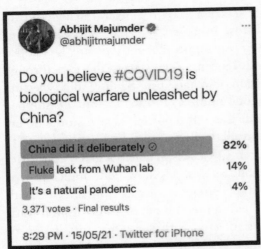

China is not an ally of India. It is not an ally of any nation in the world. It is a rogue nation. It has only one agenda—to be a global economic superpower.

In the global geopolitical arena, China will play the role of the 'big brother with a kind heart'. It will become the source of nations to stabilize themselves economically after the COVID-19 pandemic, while continuing to exert fear in most nations. The truth, however, is that China has no heart. It's agenda is completely emotionless. It will not stop until it attains global domination.

But China must be stopped at all costs.

We The Covidiots

China was the first country to try a CTA (Contact Tracing App) to curb the spread of the virus. In February 2020, it rolled out its "health code" app nationwide to control people's movements. Developed by internet giants Alibaba and Tencent, users access the app through Alipay or WeChat (China's version of WhatsApp), Baidu (China's version of Google) and input their phone number, full name and ID number. After registration, the health code uses self-reported travel histories or any suspect symptoms and automatically collects travel and medical data to assign users a red, yellow or green QR code. Whereas a green code gives users unhindered access to public spaces, a yellow code indicates that the person might have come into contact with a person infected with COVID-19 and has to be confined to their homes or an isolation facility. A red code is assigned to users infected with the virus. Installation of the health code app became more or less mandatory, resulting in broad adoption of the app among Chinese citizens.

Like Aarogya Setu, the app did receive criticism for collecting a wide range of information on central servers including personal information, location, recent contacts, health status and travel history. Every street corner has cameras and monitors that track and trace people. No one can escape from the local city governments that are doing the tracking and tracing. No one!

Germany launched its "Corona-Warn-App" in June 2020, after a long-drawn discussion about data privacy issues and the related design of the app. The download of the app in Germany is voluntary, and information exchange takes place locally on people's phones without collecting information on a central server about personal identities or locations.

In the US, rather than a top-down approach by their Central government, states and local governments cooperated with Apple and Google to develop local apps. The apps rely on Bluetooth technology and their use is voluntary. They do not collect personal information and do not upload information about personal encounters to central servers.

As of January 2021, 48 countries were using CTAs. In a global poll conducted in February 2021, 80% of Chinese, 41% of Germans and 39% of Americans strongly or somewhat accepted CTAs.

What were we doing in India for our own safety and the safety of others?

Not wearing masks outside; not maintaining minimum 6-foot distance; going to crowded places; attending events such as weddings, parties, religious gatherings, etc.; faking our temperatures by taking paracetamol (Crocin, Dolo, etc.) so that we could take flights; not disclosing potential COVID-19 symptoms even to our immediate family members; refusing to register on the Aarogya Setu CTA or mass-deleting and not use it for a year because "it's a fascist data collection system for *bhakts*"; refusing to test for COVID-19; faking negative RT-PCR test reports with Photoshop and other such software or bribing labs to give us negative reports; not disclosing our positive report even to authorities; not getting necessary treatment early … the list goes on and on.

If there were problems with the Aarogya Setu app, maybe the 50 tech geniuses we have in very kilometre of Bengaluru, Gurugram, Noida, Pune, Hyderabad, or Chennai could have built a better CTA, using blockchain technology or whatever they think is superior to what the government made. But did we do that? Despite having a year and absolutely no roadblocks?

We were also tweeting and sending WhatsApp messages criticising Modi for declaring a lockdown in 2020, asking amongst other things for malls, shops, restaurants, bars, and wine shops to be reopened. And we are surprised about a second wave.

If the Modi government clamped down on anything that **we agree with**—be it Kumbh, Ramzan, malls, restaurants, bars, weddings, we create an uproar. Maybe the government should have actually been the fascist authoritarian government we think it is.

The level of 'intellectual dishonesty' in our urban populace is astonishing; we break the rules constantly, we flout government guidelines, and then we blame and curse the government when something goes wrong.

And if one of us is infected with COVID-19, we will probably say: **"MODI STOLE MY MASK"**.

Other books by the Author

1914 NaMo or MoNa: Why is 2019 not 2014?

The 2014 elections were a combination of a very strong negative wave against the then UPA government (anti-incumbency), combined with a fairly strong wave in support of a rising regional leader, who was new to the national scene, and a bit of an enigma. This made it easy for the Modi-BJP to sweep the polls with a clear majority, the first time in 30 long years.

2019 was not going to be easy for the BJP, or Modi himself, and this book attempts to look deep into the reasons thereof.

DEMYTHSIFYING MYTHS
Demystifying 18 Myths about India

Is India 5000 years old? Did Patel deserve to be "Father of the Nation" more than Gandhi? How did the Kashmir problem start? Did Indira Gandhi win the 1971 war? Why did India give up 13,000 km² of territory to Pakistan, when China and Pakistan had seized our territories in 1962 and 1965? Why did Indira declare an Emergency in 1975? What were the mysterious deaths apart from Lal Bahadur Shashtri? What were the extramarital affairs of Nehru and Indira? Did Congress win 10 Lok Sabha elections with a majority? Are 'Coalgate' and 2G India's biggest scams? Is Hinduism a religion? What is the Hindu Rashtra? Is Rajya Sabha modelled on the British House of Lords? Why did India choose a parliamentary system of government instead of a presidential system?

72@72: 72 Unfinished Things that India@72 Needs to Do

As the name suggests, this book outlines what in the author's opinion are 72 reforms that have been pending over the years, as India reaches 72 years of independence from Great Britain (now the UK). The author says that the time has now come to finish the incomplete agenda if India truly wants to become a world superpower.

SPIES, LIES & RED TAPE
A Spy-Military-Political Fiction Thriller
based on the Indian Subcontinent

This fiction thriller starts with the premise of an alternate reality in which the party of the sitting PM loses the 2019 Lok Sabha elections. A lady with just 35 seats out of 543 in the Lok Sabha, becomes PM. She is weak on national security and takes many unpopular decisions on this front. There are a series of terror attacks, culminating in the largest-ever attack on an Indian Army base. The service/intelligence chiefs present her with a plan to hit Pakistan back, but she rejects this plan and even mocks them. They have to take matters into their own hands. What follows is how India hits back, using its military, as well as spies.

THE TIGER GETS NEW TEETH
What does the PM do when the IB, RAW, and
the NIA are constantly failing to do their jobs?

There were midnight fireworks at the home of Nationalist Party president Bianca Dalal. The NP had done very well in four state elections. It was the party's heroic return. It was an even larger triumph for the 'family', which had survived calls for its ouster. Huge explosions razed the property, the entire Dalal lineage reduced to body parts and blood splatter. Tremors would be felt throughout the country. Even the PM's biggest supporters would suspect his party. It could be the biggest threat to his career. As the world's gaze would firmly be on Mistri, would he lose his greatest asset, public opinion? He said, "I want ISSCO to investigate this."

I-SPY: A Peep into the World of Spies

Spies' lives are not as glamorous as portrayed in movies or TV shows. It is not about car chases, casinos, and 'hot' women. In reality, the work boils down to an interpretation of basic human psychology. Even though a spy learns how to get out of a dangerous situation, if s/he is resorting to fast car chases, something is wrong. The book tells the stories of the world's 20 most-powerful spy agencies, details their important missions, reveals their darkest secrets, and gives you an inside perspective of the often quite gory but thrilling '*world of spies*'. It gives you a 360° view of those spy agencies you only read about or see in a movie or TV show.

USAma: Is USA the World's Largest Terrorist?

The US is responsible for the deaths of at least 7.3 million people since WWII. In this spine-chilling book, Amit Bagaria takes us through an extraordinary journey of hundreds of illegal or immoral acts carried out by the US against 82 independent nations, which are mostly unknown to the average reader even within the US. He tries to show us how, in one way or the other, the US has bullied its way to global dominance–interfering in our day to day lives, working perhaps for the benefit of only its super powerful *Military-Industrial Complex*, which he describes in detail. Either through drones or airstrikes, surgical strikes, or full-scale military invasions, the US has created havoc in more than half the world. In other countries, different types of weapons have been used, from porn films to poison, blackmailing to torture, fake news to fake public protests, all through the CIA.

OK TATA: Why is Tata in the ICU?

In the 21 years that Rata Tata was Chairman of India's biggest business conglomerate, group revenues grew at a compounded annual growth rate (CAGR) of just 6.83%, much less than the Indian GDP growth. Many Tata companies have floundered, and the entire group survives on just one company–TCS. The book takes you through an analytical history of the House of Tatas, and also the 49 angel investments made by Ratan Tata after his 'so-called' retirement.

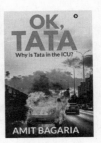

Mr. President…Yes, Prime Minister

Framers of the US Constitution chose not to adopt the British system of government as they knew its flaws. The US President has far fewer powers than the British PM. British historian Sir Sidney JM Low wrote: "An English PM, with a majority in parliament, can do what the German Emperor, the American President, and Chairmen of all Committees of the US Congress cannot do [together]." India chose to adopt the British system–all due to one man who wanted this absolute power for himself. Has the Constitution worked for India?

GARUDA PRAKASHAN BOOKS

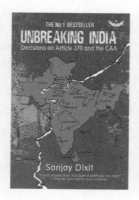

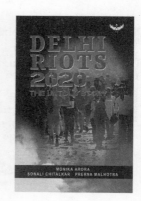

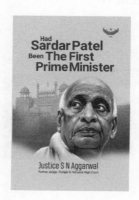

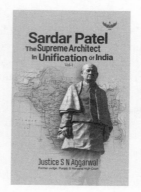

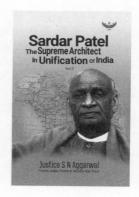

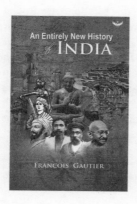

GARUDA PRAKASHAN BOOKS

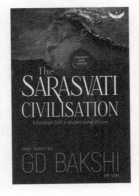

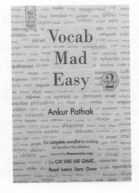

गरुड

Register:

Please register your book purchase at **grpr.in/register** to stay in touch and get informed about future books!

To order:

www.garudabooks.com

Follow us:

WEBSITE : www.garudabooks.com

FACEBOOK : www.facebook.com/garudaprakashan/

TWITTER : @garudaprakashan

INSTAGRAM : @garudabooks

YOUTUBE : /garudabooks

Contact:

EMAIL : contact@garudabooks.com

International queries:

EMAIL : international@garudabooks.com

Amit Bagaria

Amit is a serial entrepreneur-turned serial author, who has **authored 13 books** since April 2018, including **eight No.1 bestsellers**. Five of his books have been adapted in Hindi. He is also a **current affairs columnist** for a magazine and five news websites.

An out-of-the-box thinker thought leader and marketing whiz, he excels at challenging the fixed mindsets of people. He has been India's No.1 Hospital Consultant, No.1 Mall Consultant, and No.1 Residential Real Estate Consultant, apart from excelling in several other sectors.

As a Hospital Consultant, he introduced the concepts of Day Surgery Centres and Child-Birth Centres in India. Before that, he set up India's first chain of laser-based Vision Correction Centres and introduced Bone Densitometry in India for detecting Osteoporosis.

As a Mall Consultant, he planned and designed some of South India's largest malls, including India's largest mall – Sarath City Capital Mall in Hyderabad. He advised several international investors and consulted on the retail strategy for Mumbai International Airport Termial-2. As a Residential RE consultant, he planned and marketed apartments of 530–1350 square feet when the norm was 900–2300 square feet, thereby redefining the meaning of *'affordable'*.

While studying journalism in US, he was **News Editor** of the Weekly University Newspaper and was chosen **"Journalist of the Year"** in his very first year, and also received the **"All American Journalist Award"** from the American Scholastic Press Association. He also did a Journalism course at the prestigious Columbia University in New York.

Amit has also done two courses at Harvard Business School.

He has contributed four chapters in books on different subjects, more than 90 guest articles in various newspapers and magazines including *The Economic Times*, *The Indian Express* and *DNA*, as well as seven magazine cover stories.

Amit has featured in 290+ media articles in 19 countries, including 25+ newspaper front pages and 40+ TV interviews.

He has been a guest lecturer at IIM, Bangalore; Symbiosis, Pune; and Tata Institute of Social Sciences; an Anchor or Panel Moderator at 13 industry events in India, UK, Dubai and Spain, a guest speaker or panelist at several more; a member of CII and FICCI national committees, and a jury member for several award events in different sectors in India and abroad. He is also the Chairman of a 61-year-old CBSE School in Laxmangarh, Rajasthan.

Know More on: amitbagariabooks.com
Buy on Amazon: AmitBagariaBooks
Email: amit@amitbagariabooks.com

Follow him at:

 Amit Bagaria

 www.bagariaamit.com

 @amitbagaria12

 @amitbagaria

 @amitbagariabooks

 @amitbagariabooks

 Amit Bagaria

 www.linkedin.com/in/amitbagaria65/

Savio Rodrigues

Savio Rodrigues is a serial entrepreneur with business interests in media, IT, and realty.

He has over 25 years of work experience in the fields of journalism and communications. He is most respected for his as role as the Founder and Editor-in-Chief of *Goa Chronicle*, a globally recognized online news portal for its hardcore factual reportage and investigative analysis owned and operated by his startup company Kaydence Media Ventures.

He is popular panelist on TV and Web talk shows hosted in India and internationally. His nationalistic views, progressive thinking, and dedication to the pursuit of truth on matters of social justice and corruption has been admired by many Indians globally. Recently, Kayden Media has tied up with ITV Network, which owns the English news channel *NewsX* and the Hindi news channel *India News*, plus 15 other channels, to produce and host two TV shows every weekend.

Savio has authored a fiction book "*Karmic Ishq*" delving into a not often discussed subject of sexual abuse of children by family members and by strangers. This is his first non-fiction book in keeping with his penchant for research and analysis.

His philosophy is simple – "It is better to throw pebbles into a jar of water to allow the water to rise, instead of throwing a large rock and having the water splashed all around."

Follow him at:

 @princeariharan

 @princeariharan

 @saviorodrigues76

 @savio.rodrigues.54

 www.linkedin.com/in/savio-rodrigues-738183108/